BITTERSWEET GRACE

BITTERSWEET
GRACE

A Treasury of
Twentieth-Century
Religious Satire

Edited by
Walter D. Wagoner

The World Publishing Company
Cleveland and New York

Published by The World Publishing Company
2231 West 110th Street, Cleveland, Ohio 44102

Library of Congress Catalog Card Number: 66–11437

Printed in the United States of America

With love to

Mariana, Walter, Jr., Lynda and Diane

with a vast sigh
of relief that they
were not permitted a chapter
on the life and times
of the editor

Acknowledgments

Parts of the editorial introduction and commentaries were included in the Robert F. Jones Foundation Lectures I was privileged to deliver at the Austin Presbyterian Theological Seminary in January, 1966.

I am deeply indebted to Miss Edith Colton, Mrs. Christopher Meadows, and Mrs. Robert Green for their help in preparing the manuscript, and to Mr. Fredric Bogel for his skillful proofreading assistance.

Authors and publishers of works under copyright protection have been graciously cooperative in granting permission to reprint the materials in this volume. Full acknowledgment appears on the opening page of each selection.

W. D. W.

Foreword

by Bishop Gerald H. Kennedy

There are some subjects that do not easily lend themselves
to satire and humor. Anything that is taken seriously will affect
many people with an undue solemnity. They will assume a
pious air that frowns upon treating the subject with anything
less than an air of worship. Are there some subjects that are
beyond the boundaries of laughter? Is religion one of them?

Religious people—or better, church members—or even better,
the prayer-meeting crowd—will not suffer humor in the
temple gladly. Anyone who speaks of novels or plays or any
form of modern literature to religiously oriented people knows
how easy it is to shock or to be regarded as slightly improper.
It is as if men who enter the realm of religion remove themselves completely from the world and the ordinary affairs of
life. No more references to the functions of the body or to the
mystery of procreation. No more awareness of the gap between pretense and actuality. No more recognition of the
humor—sometimes slightly ribald—that results when set pat-
terns of behavior take the place of the real experience. The
growl of horror takes the place of the howl of laughter.

Now to see how wrong is this spirit and to spot the phoni-
ness of it, all we need to do is read the Bible. Nothing will keep
us from becoming pious stuffed shirts as will that wonderful

Book that uncovers our idolatry and our substitutions of solemn assemblies for the experience of the living God. Let it be noted that the Bible often does not argue seriously against our hypocrisy but simply satirizes it. The prophets ridiculed human pride and so did Jesus. Indeed, there is a book waiting to be written about Biblical satire and the wisdom of the Biblical writers who laugh at human egotism rather than attack it seriously.

So—and this is what we have been coming to—real religion is not shocked by satire but rather welcomes it. Only the people who regard maintaining an appearance as the ultimate value will be offended. It may even be argued that only the satirist takes religion as seriously as it deserves. For he is the man who is unable to endure pretense and treats cheap substitutes with the proper scorn of the prophet. Indeed, satire is not possible without some knowledge of the real thing.

Now it may be clear why I am enthusiastic about this book. *Bittersweet Grace* brings together a number of satirical passages directed at the Church, the Ministry, and the Laity. Walter Wagoner has selected the best from a wide reading for this volume, which will hold an important place on the Christian bookshelf. The professional religious worker will find many a refreshment here, and the layman will be reminded that the Gospel, besides being "good news," is also a lot of fun. And who knows? Perhaps a balloon or two will be punctured, bringing us down to earth, where we shall see ourselves not so much as a little lower than the angels, but as wayfarers partaking of the weariness and joy of the road.

It is my conviction that the Christian way is the most exciting journey a man can undertake. This is the kind of book that strengthens that conviction. For when we can no longer accept religious satire gladly, we have become one of those tiresome persons who do more than all the atheists in the world to frighten people away from Christianity.

Contents

Foreword by Bishop Gerald H. Kennedy   vii
Introduction: The Nature and Uses of
    Religious Satire   1

PART ONE: THE CLERGY   17

H. L. Mencken: *Holy Clerks*   20
Sinclair Lewis: *The Public Morals*
       Luncheon   24
James Purdy: *Plan Now to Attend*   29
Murray Kempton: *Is This All?*   34
James Gould Cozzens: *Pastoral Care*   37
Paris Leary: *The Innocent Curate*   42
Michael Frayn: *Bishop Rock*   48
J. F. Powers: *The Prince of Darkness*   51
Max Wylie: *Intercession*   60
E. L. Mascall: *The Ultra-Catholic*   65
Peter Malton: *Matrimonial Causes and*
       Reconciliation Bill   67
Gregory Wilson: *The Stained Glass Jungle*   69

PART TWO: GOD AND THE NATIONAL PANTHEON   73

William Lee Miller: *Piety Along the*
       Potomac   75
Howard Nemerov: *Sees Boom in Religion,*
       Too   80
Dialing Consensus   82

ix

Contents

PART THREE: THE CHURCH CAMOUFLAGED   85

    Shepherd Mead: *The Big Ball of Wax*   87
    Peter De Vries: *A Mature Faith*   92
    Lawrence Ferlinghetti: *Christ Climbed
          Down*   96
    John Betjeman: *In Westminster Abbey*   99
    Peter Malton: *Instant Baptism*   101
    John Bainbridge: *Religion in Texas*   103

PART FOUR: A LAUGH AT THE LAITY   109

    Osbert Sitwell: *Church Parade*   111
    Clarence Day: *My Father and His Pastors*   113
    Halford Luccock: *Like a Mighty Army*   118
    Elizabeth Berryhill: *Many Are Called, but
          Few Are Chosen*   120
    S. T. Hecht: *Oh Grave, Thy Victory*   128
    Harry Golden: *I Never Miss an Auf Probe*   135
    Werner Pelz: *And Cried Bitterly*   139
    Catholic Parlor Game   143
    Bernard Basset, S.J.: *Celia's Engagement*   146

PART FIVE: SCATTERED SHOTS   153

    C. S. Lewis: *The Clarity Hell Affords*   155
    Sean O'Casey: *The Protestant Kid Thinks
          of the Reformation*   158
    Robert Nathan: *The Devil with Love*   165
    Robert McAfee Brown: *Making the Bible
          Relevant*   170
    Anthony Towne: *God Is Dead in Georgia*   173

For Further Reading   179

Introduction:
The Nature and Uses of Religious Satire

When Peter de Vries, writing in 1964, mocks a suburban Protestant church that is so liberal that "it has made divorce into a sacrament," he is wielding the same pen held by Rabelais, who, writing in 1535, pilloried the Roman Catholic clergy: "The Popehawk who was born of the Cardinalhawks, Cardinalhawks of Bishophawks, Bishophawks of Priesthawks, Priesthawks of Clergyhawks—who had flown in from Nobreadland."

The tradition of satire of religion is one that originates well back in the Greek and Roman classical period and that has always included the most distinguished writers. Confining ourselves to the Christian Era, we can mention Dante, Chaucer, Rabelais, Erasmus, Voltaire, Pope, Swift, Shelley, Thackeray, Browning, Swinburne, Burns, to cite only the more obvious—and we are not even into the twentieth century!

It is worth noting that these writers, and others of their stature, regularly included religion among their victims. Indeed, it was often the chief target. It is a pity, therefore, that whereas satire as a comprehensive literary genre has received intense scholarly attention, there is no outstanding study of religious satire.[1]

---

[1] The reader's attention is called to the bibliography on page 179, which lists many of the better books and articles on satire.

Introduction

What is satire? Satire is an umbrella term that includes such diverse literary devices as irony, parody, invective, burlesque, ridicule, sarcasm. These modes of expression become satire when they are used to criticize and to comment, generally with the object of restoring sanity and reducing to size. The tone of most satire is a mixture of amusement and sarcasm, ranging from affectionate needling to purple invective. Satire is humor sent on an errand. The satirist wants insensitive people to see the truth. Satire has been called the literary equivalent of tar and feathers. It is wit used with a vengeance. It is comedy in the service of a moral cause. Satire has a devastating way of revealing the great gulf between reality and façade and may be described by referring to its typical targets: hypocrisy, dullness, mediocrity, stuffiness, pomp, self-righteousness and stupidity.

Satire, more than any other literary form, arouses suspicion in the reader. No sooner does one read and feel the barb than one wheels, like a dog whose tail has been pulled, to snarl at the satirist, "*Why* are you doing this?" The motives of the satirist are a constant threat to his effectiveness: motives such as defensiveness, masochism, lack of compassion for human frailty, sheer perversity, etc. But there is little point in permitting psychological voyeurism to lure the reader of great satire away from the enjoyment, the sting, and the message of the writer—from the intrinsic merits of the work itself. To be hypnotized by motive is equivalent to ranking Dostoevski's epilepsy above his genius or Einstein's mood when writing an equation above its mathematical truth.

Putting aside this exotic psychology of the satirist permits us to see clearly his chief function: that of moralist–reformer–preacher.

> The satire should be like the Porcupine
> That shoots sharp quills out in each angry line
> And wounds with blushing cheeke, and fiery eye
> Of him that heares and readeth guiltily.

G. K. Chesterton was at one with almost all analysts of satire when he wrote: "Satire may be mad and anarchic, but it presupposes a standard. When little boys in the street laugh at the fatness of some distinguished journalist, they are unconsciously assuming a standard of Greek sculpture. They are appealing to the marble Apollo."[2]

To claim that most, if not all, satirists are moral does not mean that they are moralistic (e.g., Mencken) or that they themselves lead conventionally moral lives (e.g., Swift). Rather, their preaching is effective precisely because it is so engagingly camouflaged. The good satirist approaches his quarry by stealth. But, by definition, the satirist is a man of standards. He has discriminating judgment. It would be impossible for a nihilist to be a penetrating or relevant satirist. He must have a platform, a vantage point, or, at very least, a sense of taste.

> Each with a blister on his tongue,
> Each with a crater in his tooth,
> Our nerves are fire; we have been stung
> By the tarantulas of truth.[3]

"To sting with satire the mental hindquarters" is the way Roy Campbell described his moral purpose. Sinclair Lewis declared, "I am a hedonistic missionary. I am irritated by the fact that people could be much happier than they are." "Irritated Missionary"—a marvelously apt epithet for the satirist.

Satire, having a moral function, has as its chief purpose the leveling of a particular obstacle. The satirist flails with the twin scourges of indignation and passion for truth. It must be remarked, however, that most satirists seem better at moral judgments than at philosophical ones. Mark Twain's treatment of frontier Fundamentalism is faultless; his dealing with the problem of evil is frenzied. Insofar as superstition is a perver-

---

[2] *Orthodoxy* (Garden City, N.Y.: Image Books [Doubleday & Company, Inc.], 1927), p. 42.
[3] Quoted in *Double Lives* by William Plomer (London: Jonathan Cape, 1943), p. 166.

sion of straight thinking, satire can be devastating. Here, for example, is Swift's oft-quoted paragraph about Lilliput:

> They bury their dead with their heads directly downwards, because they hold an opinion that in eleven thousand moons they are all to rise again, in which period the earth (which they conceive to be flat) will turn upside down, and by this means they shall, at their resurrection, be found ready standing on their feet. The learned among them confess the absurdity of this doctrine, but the practice still continues, in compliance to the vulgar.

How effective is satire? Like a sermon, satire is preaching for a conversion; and, like a sermon, the true impact is extremely difficult to gauge. One of the more optimistic claims for satire was voiced by Ronald Knox, English satirist and Roman Catholic priest: "Satire has an intensely remedial effect; it purifies the spiritual system of man as nothing else that is human can possibly do."[4] Although that opinion is not uncommon, Knox, like many a preacher, perhaps overestimates the power of his craft. Prolonged immersion in the literature of satire, as well as an awareness of the infinite ability of all men to dodge the shafts of ridicule, leads to a more moderate estimate of satire's results. We ought to take warning from Jonathan Swift:

> Satyr is a sort of Glass, wherein Beholders do generally discover everybody's face but their own; which is the chief reason for that kind reception it meets in the world, and that so very few are offended with it. (Preface to *The Battle of the Books*)

Richard Hofstadter's remarks are equally appropriate:

---

[4] *Essays in Satire* (London: Sheed & Ward, Ltd., 1928), p. 36. (See also Knox's delightful satire on Christian unity efforts, "Reunion All Round," in the same volume.)

We live in an age when the avant-garde has been institutionalized and deprived of its old stimulus of a stubborn and insensate opposition. . . . the large, liberal middle class audience upon which all this acceptance depends now brings to the work of the intellectual a bland, absorptive tolerance that is quite different from vital response. To the writer who has just eviscerated their way of life and their self-satisfying compromises, readers may now say "How interesting!" or even at times, "How true!" Such passive tolerance can only be infuriating. . . ."[5]

Any man with a modicum of honesty must admit, however, that skillful satire can force glib self-confidence to take stock. Above all, satire heightens our sense of skeptical self-criticism. It sharpens our insights into the world's myriad silliness—even in those areas of the world where our own dignity has been scratching for roots. Satire, when it is aimed directly at us, tends to ricochet off our invincible egotisms; but if we read enough good satire, we inevitably develop, under the tutelage of a Swift or a Butler or a Mencken, a keen eye for the meretricious in ourselves and others. Satire helps us to avoid the tawdry; its abrasive humor hones our sophistication. So long as we avoid satire's greatest danger—the temptation to cynicism—we will find unending health and sanity in its ministrations.

Age following on age, the satirists have catalogued the particular vulnerabilities of church and cult. The history is grim, hilarious, and telling. Wit serves love, and humor coats the pain: "All right, Padre," said the layman to his minister, "your idea is absurd, foolish, and ridiculous, but you've convinced me it's the will of God!" With his red pencil the satirist underlines words, gives the back of his hand to actions, that the ordinary eye might never notice.

A profile of the satirical attack on the vulnerability of a

---

[5] *Anti-intellectualism in American Life* (New York: Alfred A. Knopf, Inc., 1963), p. 418.

given era is afforded by a look at the literature portraying the Church of England in the nineteenth century. A church well-established in the fabric and class consciousness of society is always flirting with and often giving in to cultural prostitution. It is a perennial problem for any church (note how contemporary satirists pick up the same theme in America with regard to suburban Christianity and political piety). In Victorian England the Establishment was so taken for granted that God, Queen, Country, Empire, and the Church of England were all mixed together into one batter of patriotic religiosity. The many exceptional and dedicated Christians in the Church of England, including not a few who were as scandalized as any satirist, are not painted on the satirical canvas. The satirist, like the revolutionary, does not stop to praise the good or footnote the exceptions to corruption; he strikes directly at his main objects of reform. The satirist writes in declarative and exclamatory phrases; in the indicative, not in the subjunctive. In the following cultural case-study of satire, five well-known English satirists, like hounds at the kill, close in on the ecclesiastical abuses of their own day: the vaunting of religion as an exercise in respectability, the unseemly greed of clergy, the perpetuation of sinecures, the mockery of devotion soon reduced to empty formality.

PERCY BYSSHE SHELLEY (1792–1822), whose nose sniffed at the speciousness of much of the Christianity about him, turned atheist while a student at University College, Oxford. A move that today would probably stir but a ripple caused him to be expelled in 1811. His "Queen Mab," written two years after the Oxford incident, reflects his satirical revenge:

> I was an infant when my mother went
> To see an atheist burned. She took me there:
> The dark-robed priests were met around the pile;
> The multitude was gazing silently;
> And as the culprit passed with dauntless mien,
> Tempered disdain in his unaltering eye,
> Mixed with a quiet smile, shone calmly forth:
> The thirsty fire crept round his manly limbs;

His resolute eyes were scorched to blindness
    soon;
His death-pang rent my heart! the insensate mob
Uttered a cry of triumph, and I wept.
Weep not, child! cried my mother, for that man
Has said, There is no God.[6]

ALGERNON CHARLES SWINBURNE (1837–1900) attacked
hypocrisy in a manner remarkably similar to Shelley's. Swinburne was taken aback by the decadence and mustiness in
which the Church shrouded the crucified Christ. In "Before a
Crucifix" Swinburne reflects on how the sacrificing Christ had
been turned into a "dross of Christian creeds that spit on
Christ." The thrust of the poem's satire is in these lines:

> This dead God here against my face
>   Hath help for no man; who hath seen
> The good works of it, or such grace
>   As thy grace in it, Nazarene,
> As that from thy live lips which ran
> For man's sake, O thou son of man?
>
> The tree of faith ingraffed by priests
>   Puts its foul foliage out above thee,
> And round it feed man-eating beasts
>   Because of whom we dare not love thee;
> Though hearts reach back and memories ache
> We cannot praise thee for their sake.[7]

The finest satire in Victorian letters was written by SAMUEL
BUTLER (1835–1902). Butler, indeed, must be ranked with the
very greatest of satirists. The son of an Anglican clergyman
and the grandson of a bishop, Butler had been sent to Cambridge to study for Holy Orders. His religious doubts undid
those plans, but it can be argued that he performed a much

---

[6] *The Complete Poetical Works of Percy Bysshe Shelley*
(New York: Thomas Y. Crowell Company, 1878, p. 46.
[7] *Swinburne: Poems and Prose*, Everyman's Library
(London: J. M. Dent & Sons, Ltd., 1940), p. 200.

7

more salutary mission for the Church by his religious satire than he ever would have accomplished through a conventional ministry. His best lampoons of the stuffy emptiness of established religion are found in *Erewhon* (1872) and in the largely autobiographical *The Way of All Flesh*, written about 1873.

Erewhon (Nowhere) contains the devastating chapter on "Musical Banks," an allegory that compares the Church of England to a commercial banking system. Ellen Leyburn, who has written the best critical evaluation of Butler's satire, comments:

> The mockery of Victorian religion gains much from the allegorical scheme under which Butler chooses to present it. The notion of religion as a second commercial system with banks "decorated in the most profuse fashion" and all the transactions "accompanied by music" sets ideas in motion at once about self-seeking in religious motive and sentimentality in religious practice. At the same time it provides an excellent frame for subsequent details such as the maintaining of a balance in these banks by the respectable, though "the amount so kept has no direct commercial value in the outside world," the ladies going alone, "except on state occasions," and carrying their purses not exactly ostentatiously, yet just so as that those who met them should see whither they were going, and the effort to bring people back to the banks by putting fresh stained-glass windows in them and having the presidents ride in omnibuses and talk nicely to the people and remember the ages of the children and give them things when they are naughty.[8]

Butler has this to say about religion:

> Mrs. Nosnibor went on to say that I must not think there was any want of confidence in the bank because I had seen so few people there; the

---

[8] *Satiric Allegory: Mirror of Man* (New Haven, Conn.: Yale University Press, 1956), p. 100–101.

heart of the country was thoroughly devoted to these establishments, and any sign of their being in danger would bring in support from the most unexpected quarters. It was only because people knew them to be so very safe, that in some cases . . . they felt that their support was unnecessary. Moreover these institutions never departed from the safest and most approved banking principles. Thus they never allowed interest on deposit, a thing now frequently done by certain bubble companies, which by doing an illegitimate trade had drawn many customers away; and even the shareholders were fewer than formerly, owing to the innovations of these unscrupulous persons, for the Musical Banks paid little or no dividend, but divided their profits by way of bonus on the original shares once in every thirty thousand years; and as it was now only two thousand years since there had been one of these distributions, people felt that they could not hope for another in their own time and preferred investments whereby they got some more tangible return; all which, she said, was very melancholy to think of.[9]

The caricatures of life in a rectory family which Butler draws in *The Way of All Flesh* are doubly telling for their restraint and for the personal experience that they mirror. This novel is a basic source document for any social historian who seeks to comprehend that era. Theobald is the Rector; Christina, his wife. Their self-righteousness is the more frightening because they are not aware of it:

I should doubt whether he ever got as far as doubting the wisdom of his Church upon any single matter. His scent for possible mischief was tolerably keen; so was Christina's, and it is likely that if either of them detected in him or herself the first faint symptoms of a want of faith they were nipped no less peremptorily in the bud,

---

[9] *Erewhon* (New York: E. P. Dutton & Co., Inc., 1917), p. 151.

than signs of self-will in Ernest were—and I should imagine more successfully. Yet Theobald considered himself, and was generally considered to be, and indeed perhaps was, an exceptionally truthful person; indeed he was generally looked upon as an embodiment of all those virtues which make the poor respectable and the rich respected. In the course of time he and his wife became persuaded even to unconsciousness, that no one could even dwell under their roof without deep cause for thankfulness. Their children, their servants, their parishioners must be fortunate *ipso facto* that they were theirs. There was no road to happiness here or hereafter, but the road that they had themselves travelled, no good people who did not think as they did upon every subject, and no reasonable person who had wants the gratification of which would be inconvenient to them—Theobald and Christina.[10]

Then there is the much quoted passage in the same novel, with the acrid comments on the wallpaper in Theobald's study:

It happened that some years previously, a swarm of bees had taken up their abode in the roof of the house under the slates, and had multiplied so that the drawing-room was a good deal frequented by these bees during the summer, when the windows were open. The drawing-room paper was of a pattern which consisted of bunches of red and white roses, and I saw several bees at different times fly up to these bunches and try them, under the impression that they were real flowers; having tried one bunch, they tried the next, and the next, and the next, till they reached the one that was nearest the ceiling, then they went down bunch by bunch as they had ascended, till they were stopped by the back of the

---

[10] *The Way of All Flesh* (London: Jonathan Cape, Ltd., 1961), p. 98.

sofa; on this they ascended bunch by bunch to
the ceiling again; and so on, and so on till I was
tired of watching them. As I thought of the
family prayers being repeated night and morning, week by week, month by month, and year
by year, I could not help thinking how like it
was to the way in which the bees went up the
wall and down the wall, bunch by bunch, without ever suspecting that so many of the associated
ideas could be present, and yet the main idea be
wanting hopelessly, and for ever.[11]

Another instance of satirical comment on a similar phenom-
enon, but in a lighter vein, is a poem by W. S. GILBERT
(1836–1911)—the same Gilbert who, with Sullivan, set to
music so much witty sarcasm. In this poem, "The Reverend
Simon Magus," the vicar, eager to get a plush living, consults
with an ecclesiastical real-estate agent:

> A rich advowson, highly prized,
> For private sale was advertised;
> And many a parson made a bid;
> The REVEREND SIMON MAGUS did.
>
> He sought the agent's: "Agent, I
> Have come prepared at once to buy
> (If your demand is not too big)
> The Cure of Otium-cum-Digge."
>
> "Ah!" said the agent, "*there's* a berth—
> The snuggest vicarage on earth;
> No sort of duty (so I hear),
> And fifteen hundred pounds a year!
>
> "If on the price we should agree,
> The living soon will vacant be:
> The good incumbent's ninety-five
> And cannot very long survive.

---

[11] *Ibid.*, p. 118.

"See—here's his photograph—you see,
He's in his dotage." "Ah, dear me!
Poor soul!" said Simon. "His decease
Would be a merciful release!"

The agent laughed—the agent blinked—
The agent blew his nose and winked
And poked the parson's ribs in play—
It was the agent's vulgar way.[12]

Our final illustration of satire of Victorian religion comes from the poetry of THOMAS HARDY (1840–1928). Most of Hardy's writings, both prose and poetry, are overcast with tragedy and irony. He thus moved rather easily into satire. In the poem "A Refusal," Hardy blisters the Dean of Westminster Abbey for refusing permission to place a memorial tablet to Lord Byron in the Poets' Corner because its presence would be offensive to piety.

Said the grave Dean of Westminster:
Mine is the best minster
Seen in Great Britain,
As many have written:
So therefore I cannot
Rule here if I ban not
Such liberty-taking
As movements for making
Its greyness environ
The memory of Byron,
Which some are demanding
Who think them of standing,
But in my own viewing
Require some subduing
For tendering suggestions
On Abbey-wall questions
That must interfere here
With my proper sphere here,

---

[12] *The Bab Ballads* (London: Macmillan and Co., Ltd., 1906), p. 356.

And bring to disaster
This fane and its master,
Whose dict is but Christian
Though nicknamed Philistian.[13]

The Established Church of Victorian England has been cited as a case study because writers as notable as the ones quoted here (plus Austen, Trollope, Thackeray, Browning, *et al.*) found it such fair game. But each age has its foibles, and satire teaches us that it is blind self-righteousness to deny them. Whether it is Mark Twain and Finley Peter Dunne (Mr. Dooley) jumping on the excesses of Christian Science, or Stephen Leacock cartooning the philistine rivalry between the churches of St. Asaph and St. Osoph, or Donald Ogden Stewart portraying Uncle Frederick with one hand on the First National Bank and the other on the First Presbyterian Church, each time and place and faith is sure to be watched carefully and mercilessly by those profane prophets, the satirists.

What are some of the characteristics of twentieth-century American religious satire? It is immediately obvious that in a land of folksy and largely uncritical denominationalism, American Christians, Protestant and Catholic, reflect less maturity in satirical matters than do Christians in England. In any time and place religious satire must run an extraordinarily delicate course as it threads its way through touchiness, righteousness, and cultural symbols of the Almighty. In moralistic America this is doubly the case. Since religious satire deals with the idolatries of the godly, it necessarily manhandles some of the deepest and dearest human convictions—often those which give people their sense of identity. When Mark Twain wrote, "I never count any prospective chickens when I know that Providence knows where the nest is," he had thrown a spit ball on someone's altar. When Mencken averred that "a Bishop is a Christian who has attained to a higher ecclesiastical status

---

[13] *Collected Poems of Thomas Hardy* (New York: The Macmillan Company, 1937), pp. 769–771.

13

than Jesus Christ," it is barely possible that there was no laughter even in the pews farthest back. Most Americans, *genus religiosum,* become far too nervous in the presence of any criticism, sober or satirical, of anything associated with the holy. We have not lived with satire as long as the British, and we are still more apt to take umbrage than to learn. Nietzsche's acidic epigram, "I like not these coquettish bugs who in their insatiable desire to smell of the infinite make the infinite smell of bugs," will hardly be printed on the velveteen banners of a revival meeting.

Furthermore, it is worth noting that most American satirists of religion have only a casual personal commitment, if any, to the Church. The heavy moralistic ethos and the pietistic seriousness of American Christianity is not a congenial home for those who revel in the healthy secularities of life, as do most satirists. There is evidence to support the hope that this situation will change rapidly.

Until recently American religious satire has also been characterized by an overwhelming obsession with the crude, perspiring, uneducated, and often salacious evangelist. Our satirists have had an easy time shooting fundamentalist fish in the cultural barrel. This foray is our counterpart to the English satirist's barrage on the preciousness of over-bred, fox-hunting parsons. However, the target of American satirists has more recently been shifting to the suburban church, as satirist joins forces with sociologist. With population changes going as they are, it can be assumed that some of the new experiments in urban churches will shortly receive their due satirical attention.

In the United States satire has been shaped also by the fact that American Christianity has had no religious Establishment, no State Church, no overt combination of Church officialdom and political oligarchy. This has meant that the satirist has lacked the fertile field provided by the histories of England, France, Italy, Spain, and Germany. The visibility of a religious Establishment is open season for the caricaturist. In America, as this anthology indicates, the barbs are aimed more at persons and at attitudes.

14

Related to the absence of a religious Establishment is the absence of anticlericalism as a result of satire.[14] This may speak well for the behavior of most clergy. But, in any event, there has never been the virulent public desire to "hang the last priest in the entrails of the last king." Lacking both an Established Church and a related anticlerical tradition, the American satirist of religion has a greater difficulty in separating his institutional and individual criticism from what would in the public mind sound like a criticism of God. That is why it is important to recall that, although satirists may not always be churchmen, they are often animated by valid religious instincts and sympathies. They are concerned with removing the abuses done in the name of God or Christ. To the satirist, as someone has noted, blasphemy may be a more religious act than piety. The American satirist tends to be viewed unfairly as the village atheist. Religious satire is regarded too often as a vendetta on faith.

Finally, the task of the American satirist is made doubly complicated by the peculiar manner in which the American Christian and Jew has homogenized his culture and his faith. This means that a satirical attack on some scandal of faith may be construed as an affront to patriotic loyalty. When religious symbols and myths are so diffused in the common life, a satirist may hesitate lest he be struck as dead as the Israelite who touched the Ark of the Covenant. Henry Carlisle remarks that "the American satirist tends to avoid all but the most obvious abuses and, generally, to avoid the subject of religion altogether." Quoting Malcolm Muggeridge, Carlisle continues:

> The area of life in which ridicule is permissible is steadily shrinking, and a dangerous tendency is becoming manifest to take ourselves with undue seriousness. . . . Irreverence is decidedly out of fashion, and the clown or satirist, if he is to con-

---

[14] See James H. Smylie and Walter D. Wagoner, "Clericalism and Anti-clericalism," *The Christian Century* (October 25, 1961), p. 1264.

15

tinue in his business, must keep a careful eye on
his targets lest they frown unduly.[15]

The aim of the editor in compiling this anthology has been
that of illustrating how the twentieth-century satirist of religion goes about stalking the old, old prey: religious pride, holy
pomp and circumstance, theological silliness. The audience to
whom this collection is addressed is a markedly growing
number of Catholics, Jews, and Protestants, both lay and
clerical, whose religious maturity seeks out this type of sand-
paper honesty. These are the men and women who realize that
when a human being seeks to talk about God there is a
constant need for a jester in the temple court. In this audience
there are certainly those who have only one foot within the
temple, or who, like Voltaire, will end up by being buried half
in the churchyard, half out. These are the God-fearers, those
people in our culture with a strong ambivalence about religion.
Satire will appeal to them, not as a cheap opportunity to jump
on the Church, but as a reassuring sign that institutionalized
religion, insofar as it harbors and heeds the satirist, may not be
beyond recall. And undoubtedly a few of the readers of this
volume will be those who clutch satire of religion in the same
fashion that a pornographer regales himself with the salacious.
That always happens: and it is in itself a deserving subject of
satire.

Satire of religion is a profane grace, a bittersweet grace. It
ministers sanity. It subdues pride, even as it does delightful
damage to the pretentiousness of those who have taken God
into partnership without His consent. Good satire forces each
age to shake the manifestations of its faiths through the sieve
of laughter, thus enabling us to perceive the more accurately
the lumps and dirt which have been mixed with the gold.
Appreciation of religious satire is a mark of maturity and
confidence. But even then, just as we begin to preen our
feathers, the satirist, thank God, will raise before our eyes his
well-placed mirror.

---

[15] *American Satire in Prose and Verse* (New York:
Random House, Inc., 1962), p. 15.

16

Part One:

The Clergy

At the Shrine of Lourdes in France there are three public baths: one for women, one for men, and one for priests. The Gallican anticlerical instinct is not without witness even amid the pious. It is another example of the criticism which the clergy, deservedly or undeservedly, must endure. As the most visible leaders of religion, priests, ministers, and rabbis are fair game for cynics who feel that religion is a dreary fraud, for idealists who will not compromise with human nature, and for critics and satirists who want no nonsense. In sheer number of pages and words, the lion's share of religious satire has been focused on the clergy. In a religious age clergymen got such doubtful billing even above the politicians. In our age they run a distant fourth to generals, cabinet members, and mothers.

The first group of selections is representative of what has long been the major target for American religious satire: the rube-evangelist. The nineteenth-century frontier missionary devised evangelistic methods which were highly effective in a mobile, semi-literate society. Those methods were easily abused when salesmanship, piety, and personality joined hands

17

to take advantage of the "you're-either-saved-or-you're-not" type of simplistic theology and morality which had been formulated. H. L. MENCKEN, despite a streak of vaudeville showmanship, is still acclaimed by many as the greatest twentieth-century American satirist. He was hypnotized by the "Boobus Americanus" expression of religion in contemporary culture, and he was merciless in his caricatures of it. SINCLAIR LEWIS, whose twenty-two novels satirize everyone except novelists, described in greater detail what Mencken had shot on the dead run. The Reverend Elmer Gantry is now a classic character in American literature, not only for what he says about a bankrupt ministry, but also because the George Babbitts of Elmer's congregation felt that their minister was a "great guy." "JAMES PURDY," said John Cowper Powys, "is a writer with remarkable insight into the diabolical cruelties and horrors that lurk all the time under our conventional skin." In this sketch Mr. Purdy reveals, with more depth of insight than either Mencken or Lewis, just what it is that lurks under the skin of God's ballyhoo artists. MURRAY KEMPTON, a secular journalist of great artistry, easily could have done the clichéd hatchet job on a Billy Graham rally. Instead, he puts many Christian commentators to shame by the surgical deftness with which he dissects the whole affair and reveals its awful emptiness.

The next montage portrays that species of well-educated, cleverly honed clergy whose very eagerness to be sophisticated becomes their undoing. JAMES GOULD COZZENS fashions a satirical vignette, indirect and casual, around a *tête-à-tête* between the New York City Episcopal clergyman, Cudlipp, and Geraldine, a married socialite parishioner who has become pregnant in an extramarital escapade. Against a background of sherry and sleeping pills Cudlipp does his pastoral counseling. PARIS LEARY, a college teacher, brings before us the Reverend Dr. Groby, High Church Episcopal priest, as he slithers on his rabat toward a bishopric. Mr. Leary's insights have the frightening accuracy of a literary fluoroscope revealing the minutest machinations of pride. MICHAEL FRAYN, columnist for the

18

London Observer, is a good example of the British delight in burlesque: Bishop Rock's only major fault is that in bringing the Gospel to the Beatle generation he has obscured the timeless in his very hurry to be timely.

J. F. POWERS' writings have been largely concerned with Roman Catholic priests. His novel *Morte D'Urban* was called the *Babbitt* of contemporary Catholic community life. He displays in this portion of *Prince of Darkness* a satire which is compounded of love and exasperation. With beautiful finesse he gets behind and under all the stereotypes of the priest. MAX WYLIE, and his brother Philip, are the sons of a Presbyterian minister who at one time was a pastor in a small Midwestern university town. There must be much autobiographical memory in his story of the world as it appeared to the eyes of the pastor's twelve-year-old son, Gilson. E. L. MASCALL, one of the most highly regarded theologians in the Anglo-Catholic wing of the Church of England, has a sense of humor refreshing enough to laugh at his own kind. PETER MALTON's *Matrimonial Causes and Reconciliation Bill* gives us a Church of England companion piece which roasts the logic of a moral theology that will admit only adultery as the sole justification for divorce, never mutual consent. The solution is poetic justice. GREGORY WILSON is a pseudonym for a Methodist minister-author who has the courage to lambaste the entrepreneurial jungle of his denomination, but who himself must be asked the reason for his literary mask. His sketch is a church version of the gray-flannel-suit–executive-suite school of reporting.

H. L. Mencken

Holy Clerks

Around no class of men do more false assumptions cluster than around the rev. clergy, our lawful commissioners at the Throne of Grace. I proceed at once to a crass example: the assumption that clergymen are necessarily religious. Obviously, it is widely cherished, even by clergymen themselves. The most ribald of us, in the presence of a holy clerk, is a bit self-conscious, reticent and awed. I am myself given to criticizing Divine Providence somewhat freely, but in the company of the rector of my parish, even at the "Biertisch," I tone down my animadversions to a level of feeble and polite remonstrance. I know the fellow too well, of course, to have any actual belief in his piety. He is, in fact, rather less pious than the average right-thinking Americano, and I doubt gravely that the sorceries he engages in professionally every day awaken in him any emotion more lofty than boredom. I have heard him pray for Coolidge, for the heathen and for rain, but I have never heard him pray for himself. Nevertheless, the public assumption that he is highly devout, though I dispute it, colors all my intercourse with him, and deprives him of hearing some of my most searching and intelligent observations.

All that is needed to expose the hollowness of this ancient delusion is to consider the chain of causes which brings a young man to taking Holy orders. Is it, in point of fact, an irresistible religious impulse that sets him to studying exegetics, homiletics and the dog-Greek of the New Testament, and an irresistible religious impulse only, or is it something quite different? I believe that it is something quite different, and that something may be described briefly as a desire to shine in the world without too much effort. The young theologue, in brief, is commonly an ambitious but somewhat lazy and incompetent fellow, and he studies theology instead of medicine or law because it offers a quicker and easier route to an assured job and public respect. The sacred sciences may be nonsensical bores, but they at least have the vast virtue of short-circuiting, so to speak, the climb up the ladder of security. The young doctor, for a number of years after he graduates, either has to work for nothing or to content himself with the dregs of practice, and the young lawyer, unless he has unusual influence or complete atrophy of the conscience, often teeters on the edge of actual starvation. But the young divine is a safe and distinguished man the moment he is ordained; indeed, his popularity, especially among the faithful who are fair, is often greater at that moment than it ever is afterward. His livelihood is assured instantly. At one stroke, he becomes a person of dignity and importance, eminent in his community, deferred to even by those who question his magic, and vaguely and pleasantly feared by those who credit it.

These facts, you may be sure, are not concealed from ambitious young men of the sort I have mentioned. Such young men have eyes, and even a capacity for ratiocination. They observe the nine sons of the police sergeant: one, a priest at twenty-five, with a fine house to live in, invitations to all christenings and birthday parties for miles around, and plenty of time to go to the ball game on summer afternoons; the others, struggling desperately to make their livings as piano-movers, tin-roofers, motormen or bootleggers. They observe the young Methodist dominie in his Ford sedan, flitting about among the women while their husbands labor down in the yards district, a clean collar around his neck, a solid meal of

21

fried chicken in his gizzard, and his name in the local paper every day. They observe the Baptist dervish in his white necktie, raiding saloons, touring the bawdyhouses and raising hell generally, his tabernacle packed every Sunday night, a noble clink of silver in his collection plates, and a fat purse for him now and then from the Ladies Aid or the Ku Klux Klan. Only crazy women ever fall in love with young doctors or lawyers, but every young clergyman, if he is so inclined, may have a whole harem, and with infinitely less danger than a struggling lawyer, a bootlegger or a bank clerk runs every day. Even if he is celibate, the gals bathe him in their smiles; in truth the more celibate he is, the more attention he gets from them. No wonder his high privileges and immunities propagate the sin of envy! No wonder there are still candidates for the holy shroud, despite the vast growth of atheism among us!

It seems to me that the majority of the young men who are thus sucked into holy orders are not actually pious at all, but rather somewhat excessively realistic—that genuine piety is far more apt to keep a youth out of the pulpit than to take him into it. The true devotee, frequenting the sacred edifice constantly, becomes too familiar with the daily duties of a clergyman to see any religious satisfaction in them. In the main, they have nothing to do with religion at all, but are basically social or commercial. In so far as a clergyman works at all, he works as the general manager of a corporation, and only too often it is in financial difficulties and rent by factions among the stockholders. His specifically religious duties are of a routine and monotonous nature, and must needs depress him mightily, as a surgeon is depressed by the endless snaring of tonsils and excision of appendices. He debases patriotism as a lady of joy debases love. He becomes, in the end, quite anaesthetic to religion, and even hostile to it. The fact is made distressingly visible by the right reverends, the bench of bishops. For a bishop to fall on his knees spontaneously and begin to pray to God would make almost as great a scandal as if he mounted his throne in a bathing-suit. The piety of the ecclesiastic, on such high levels, becomes wholly formal and theoretical. The servant of God has been lifted so near to the saints and become so familiar with the inner workings of the divine machinery that the sense of awe and wonder has oozed out of him. He can no more undergo a genuine religious experience than a veteran scene-shifter can laugh at the sneezes of the First Gravedigger. It is, perhaps, well that this is so. If the higher clergy were actually religious, some of their own sermons and pastoral epistles would scare them to death.

Sinclair Lewis

The Public Morals
Luncheon

As important as publicity to Elmer was the harassing drive of finance.

He had made one discovery superb in its simple genius—the best way to get money was to ask for it, hard enough and often enough. To call on rich men, to set Sunday School classes in competition against one another, to see that every one received pledge-envelopes, these were all useful and he pursued them earnestly. But none of them was so useful as to tell the congregation every Sunday what epochal good Wellspring and its pastor were doing, how much greater good they could do if they had more funds, and to demand their support now, this minute.

His official Board was charmed to see the collections increasing even faster than the audience. They insisted that the bishop send Elmer back to them for another year—indeed for many years—and they raised Elmer's salary to forty-five hundred dollars.

And in the autumn they let him have two subordinates—the Reverend Sidney Webster, B.A., B.D., as Assistant Pastor, and Mr. Henry Wink, B.A., as Director of Religious Education.

Mr. Webster had been secretary to Bishop Toomis, and it was likely that he would some day be secretary of one of the

200 W 125
C. 1

Sinclair Lewis: *The Public Morals Luncheon*

powerful church boards—the board of publications, the board of missions, the board of temperance and morals. He was a man of twenty-eight; he had been an excellent basketball player in Boston University; he was tight-mouthed as a New England president, efficient as an adding machine, and cold as the heart of a bureaucrat. If he loved God and humanity-in-general with rigid devotion, he loved no human individual; if he hated sin, he was too contemptuous of any actual sinner to hate him—he merely had no vices. He was also competent. He could preach, get rid of beggars, be quietly devout in death-bed prayers, keep down church expenses, and explain about the Trinity.

Henry Wink had a lisp and he told little simpering stories, but he was admirable in the direction of the Sunday School, vacation Bible schools, and the Epworth League.

With Mr. Webster and Mr. Wink removing most of the church detail from him, Elmer became not less but more occupied. He no longer merely invited the public, but galloped out and dragged it in. He no longer merely scolded sin. He gratifyingly ended it.

When he had been in Zenith for a year and three-quarters, Elmer formed the Committee on Public Morals, and conducted his raids on the red-light district.

It seemed to him that he was getting less publicity. Even his friend, Colonel Rutherford Snow, owner of the *Advocate-Times*, explained that just saying things couldn't go on being news; news was essentially a report of things done.

"All right, I'll do things, by golly, now that I've got Webster and Wink to take care of the glad hand for the brethren!" Elmer vowed.

He received an inspiration to the effect that all of a sudden, for reasons not defined, "things have gotten so bad in Zenith, immorality is so rampant in high places and low, threatening the morals of youth and the sanctity of domesticity, that it is not enough for the ministry to stand back warning the male-factors, but a time now to come out of our dignified seclusion and personally wage open war on the forces of evil."

He said these startling things in the pulpit, he said them in

25

an interview, and he said them in a letter to the most important clergymen in town, inviting them to meet with him to form a Committee on Public Morals and make plans for open war.

The devil must have been shaken. Anyway, the newspapers said that the mere threat of the formation of the committee had caused "a number of well-known crooks and women of bad reputation to leave town." Who these scoundrels were, the papers did not say.

The Committee was to be composed of the Reverends Elmer Gantry and Otto Hickenlooper, Methodists; G. Prosper Edwards, Congregationalist; John Jennison Drew, Presbyterian; Edmund St. Vincent Zahn, Lutheran; James F. Gomer, Disciples; Father Matthew Smeesby, Catholic; Bernard Amos, Jewish; Hosea Jessup, Baptist; Willis Fortune Tate, Episcopalian; and Irving Tillish, Christian Science reader; with Wallace Umstead, the Y.M.C.A. secretary, four moral laymen, and a lawyer, Mr. T. J. Rigg.

They assembled at lunch in a private dining-room at the palatial Zenith Athletic Club. Being clergymen, and having to prove that they were also red-blooded, as they gathered before lunch in the lobby of the club they were particularly boisterous in shouting to passing acquaintances, florist and doctors and wholesale plumbers. To one George Babbitt, a real estate man, Dr. Drew, the Presbyterian, clamored, "Hey, Georgie! Got a flask along? Lunching with a bunch of preachers, and I reckon they'll want a drink!"

There was great admiration on the part of Mr. Babbitt, and laughter among all the clergymen, except the Episcopal Mr. Tate and the Christian Scientific Mr. Tillish.

The private dining-room at the club was a thin red apartment with two pictures of young Indian maidens of Lithuanian origin sitting in native costumes, which gave free play to their legs, under a rugged pine-tree against a background of extremely high mountains. In Private Dining-room A, beside them, was a lunch of the Men's Furnishers Association, addressed by S. Garrison Siegel of New York on "The Rented Dress Suit Business and How to Run It in a High-Class Way."

The incipient Committee on Public Morals sat about a long

26

narrow table in bentwood chairs, in which they were always vainly trying to tilt back. Their table did not suggest debauchery and the demon rum. There were only chilly and naked-looking goblets of ice water.

They lunched, gravely on consommé, celery, roast lamb, which was rather cold, mashed potatoes, which were arctic, Brussels sprouts which were overstewed, ice cream, which was warm; with very large cups of coffee, and no smoking afterward.

Elmer began, "I don't know who is the oldest among us, but certainly no one in this room has had a more distinguished or more valuable term of Christian service than Dr. Edwards, of Pilgrim Congregational, and I know you'll join me in asking him to say grace before meat."

The table conversation was less cheerful than the blessing.

They all detested one another. Every one knew of some cases in which each of the others had stolen, or was said to have tried to steal, some parishioner, to have corrupted his faith and appropriated his contributions. Dr. Hickenlooper and Dr. Drew had each advertised that he had the largest Sunday School in the city. All of the Protestants wanted to throw ruinous questions about the Immaculate Conception at Father Smeesby, and Father Smeesby, a smiling dark man of forty, had ready, in case they should attack the Catholic Church, the story of the ant who said to the elephant, "Move over, who do you think you're pushing?" All of them, except Mr. Tillish, wanted to ask Mr. Tillish how he'd ever been fooled by this charlatan, Mary Baker Eddy, and all of them, except the rabbi, wanted to ask Rabbi Amos why the Jews were such numbskulls as not to join the Christian faith.

They were dreadfully cordial. They kept their voices bland, and smiled too often, and never listened to one another. Elmer, aghast, saw that they would flee before making an organization if he did not draw them together. And what was the one thing in which they were all joyously interested? Why, vice! He'd begin the vice rampage now instead of waiting till the business meeting after lunch.

He pounded on the table, and demanded, "Most of you have

27

been in Zenith longer than myself. I admit ignorance. It is true that I have unearthed many dreadful, *dreadful* cases of secret sin. But you gentlemen, who know the town so much better—am I right? Are conditions as dreadful as I think, or do I exaggerate?"

All of them lighted up and, suddenly looking on Elmer as a really nice man after all, they began happily to tell of their woeful discoveries. . . . The blood-chilling incident of the father who found in the handbag of his sixteen-year-old daughter improper pictures. The suspicion that at a dinner of war veterans at the Leroy House there had danced a young lady who wore no garments save slippers and a hat.

"I know all about that dinner—I got the details from a man in my church—I'll tell you about it if you feel you ought to know," said Dr. Gomer.

They looked as though they decidedly felt that they ought to know. He went into details, very, and at the end Dr. Jessup gulped, "Oh, that Leroy House is absolutely a den of iniquity! It ought to be pulled!"

"It certainly ought to! I don't think I'm cruel," shouted Dr. Zahn, the Lutheran, "but if I had my way, I'd burn the proprietor of that joint at the stake!"

All of them had incidents of shocking obscenity all over the place—all of them except Father Smeesby, who sat back and smiled, the Episcopal Dr. Tate, who sat back and looked bored, and Mr. Tillish, the healer, who sat back and looked chilly. In fact it seemed as though, despite the efforts of themselves and the thousands of other inspired and highly trained Christian ministers who had worked over it ever since its foundation, the city of Zenith was another Sodom. But the alarmed apostles did not appear to be so worried as they said they were. They listened with almost benign attention while Dr. Zahn, in his German accent, told of alarming crushes between the society girls whom he knew so well from dining once a year with his richest parishioner.

They were all, indeed, absorbed in vice to a degree gratifying to Elmer.

28

James Purdy

Plan Now to Attend

[*Note: Mr. Graitop is America's leading mass evangelist. Fred, his former college roommate, meets him in a hotel lobby and lures Graitop into the bar for a drink.*]

Mr. Graitop did not say anything. Everybody had heard of his great success in introducing "new Religion" to America so that when many people thought of "new Religion" they thought immediately of Graitop.

It was a surprise to Fred to remember that Graitop had been a practicing atheist in the college quadrangles, for he remembered it only this instant.

"You were one, you know," Fred said almost viciously.

"We are always moving toward the one path," Graitop said dreamily, drinking his second drink.

Although Fred was a hard drinker, he had swiftly lost all his appetite for it, and he knew that it was not the early hour. Very often at this hour, setting out as a salesman, he was completely oiled.

"Is it the new religion that keeps you looking so kind of embalmed and youthful," Fred said, as though he had had his usual five brandies.

"Fred," Mr. Graitop said on his third drink, with mechanical composure, "it is the only conceivable path."

"I liked you better as an infidel," Fred said. "You looked

more human then, too, and older. I suppose you go to all the football games now that you're a famous man."

"I suppose I see a good many," Graitop said.

"Fred," Mr. Graitop said, closing his eyes softly, and as he did so he looked remarkably older, "why can't you come with us this time?"

Fred did not know what to say because he did not exactly understand the question.

"There is no real reason to refuse. You are a living embodiment of what we all are without *the* prop."

"I'm not following you now," Fred replied.

"You are, but you won't let yourself," Graitop said, opening his eyes and finishing his third drink. He tapped the glass as though it had been an offering for Fred.

Fred signaled for another drink for Graitop just as in the past he would have for himself. His own first drink remained untouched, which he could not understand, except he felt nauseated. He realized also that he hated the great man and had always hated him.

"Well, what am I?" Fred said as he watched Graitop start his fourth drink.

"The embodiment of the crooked stick that would be made straight," the great man replied.

"You really do go for that, don't you. That is," Fred continued, "you have made that talk part of your life."

"There is no talk involved," Mr. Graitop said. "No talk, Fred."

I wonder why the old bastard is drinking so much, Fred nearly spoke aloud. Then: "Graitop, nobody has ever understood what makes you tick."

"That is unimportant," his friend replied. "It, too, is talk."

"Nobody ever even really liked you, though I don't suppose anybody ever liked St. Paul either."

"Of course, Fred, you are really with us in spirit," Graitop said as though he had not heard the last statement.

Fred looked at his drink which seemed cavernous as a well.

"Graitop," he said stonily, "you discovered Jesus late. Later than me. I'd had all that when I was twelve. . . ."

"You're part of the new movement and your denying it here to me only confirms it," Mr. Graitop informed him.

"I don't want to be part of it," Fred began and he tasted some of his drink, but Graitop immediately interrupted.

"It isn't important that you don't want to be part: you are part and there is nothing you can do about it. You're with us."

"I couldn't be with you," Fred began, feeling coming up within him a fierce anger, and he hardly knew at what it was directed, for it seemed to be larger than just his dislike, suspicion, and dread of Graitop.

Then Mr. Graitop must have realized what only the bartender had sensed from the beginning, that he was not only drunk but going to be sick. Fred had not noticed it at all, for he felt that he had suddenly been seized and forced to relive the impotence and stupidity of his adolescence.

With the bartender's help, he assisted Mr. Graitop out of the bar. In the elevator, Graitop grew loud and belligerent and shouted several times: "It's the only path, the only way."

"What is your room number?" Fred said hollow-voiced as they got out of the elevator.

"You are really part of our group," Graitop replied.

Fred took the key out of Graitop's pocket and nodded to the woman at the desk who stared at them.

"You are completely oiled," Fred informed Graitop when the latter had lain down on the bed. "And yet it doesn't convince me any more than your preaching."

"I wonder if I had appointments," Graitop said weakly. "I was to speak to some of our people. . . ."

"I wonder which of us feels more terrible," Fred replied. "This meeting after twenty years (and he shouted the number) has been poison to both of us. We hate one another and everything we stand for. At least I hate you. You are probably too big a fraud to admit hate. I'm saying this cold sober, too, although I guess just the inside of a bar oils me up."

31

The Clergy

"You are a living embodiment of sin and sorrow and yet you are dear to us," Graitop said, looking at the ceiling.

"What the hell are you the living embodiment of, what?" Fred said and he began loosening his friend's clothing. Before he knew it, he had completely undressed Mr. Graitop as mechanically as he undressed himself when drunk. As his friend lay there, a man of at least forty, Fred was amazed to see that he looked like a boy of sixteen. Almost nothing had touched him in the world. So amazed and objective was Fred's surprise that he took the bed lamp and held it to his face and body to see if he was not deceived and this forty-year-old man was not actually a palimpsest of slightly hidden decay and senility. But the light revealed nothing but what his eye had first seen—a youth untouched by life and disappointment.

He looked so much like God or something mythological that before he knew what he was doing Fred Parker had kissed him dutifully on the forehead.

"Why did you do that?" Mr. Graitop said, touching the place with his finger, and his voice was almost human.

Fred Parker sat down in a large easy chair and loosened his necktie. He did not answer the question because he had not heard it. He felt intoxicated and seriously unwell.

"How in hell do you live, Graitop?" he said almost too softly to be heard. "Are you married and do you have kids?"

"Yes, yes," Graitop replied, and he began to drivel now from his mouth.

Fred got up and wiped off his lips, and put the covers over him.

"A missionary," Fred Parker said. "But of what?"

"Don't be a fool," Graitop said sleepily. Suddenly he was asleep.

Fred Parker watched him again angrily from the chair.

"Who in hell are you, Graitop?" he shouted from the chair. "Why in hell did I run into you. Why in hell did I speak to you. . . . Why don't you look and act like other men?"

Fred called room service for ice, whiskey, and water. He

began immediately the serious drinking he should not have been without all morning.

"When the bastard is conscious, I will ask him who he is and what he means to do."

"It's all right, Fred," Mr. Graitop said from time to time from the bed. "You are really with us, and it's all all right."

"I wish you wouldn't use that goddam language, Graitop," he said. "You don't have the personality for a missionary. Too young and dead looking. Too vague."

From the bed there came sounds like a small boy sleeping.

Murray Kempton

Is This All?

Before I say another word about Billy Graham's opening, I should like to say that, if Jesus Christ crucified for our sins was good enough for Johann Sebastian Bach and Fyodor Dostoievski and Georges Rouault, He is much too good for the likes of me, and I shall make no sport of any honest prophet of His.

Billy Graham is a decent, honorable man—although a feeble preacher by any proper standards—and he is much too decent to be forced by his commitment to live even six weeks in a town whose stores hang dirty Christmas cards in their windows in December. The faithful who walked down Eighth Avenue from the Garden last night passed, blessedly unseeing, by a store which displayed the Holy Bible, Stanley High's book on Billy Graham, some bookkeeper's rewrite of various epistles of Saint Paul, and the latest vision of Norman Vincent Peale side by side with works geared more to its ordinary clientele like *Are You Over Sex-ty?* and *Sex-ation, 1957.*

It is not my recollection that the money-changers were peddling Cretan postcards on the side; I think the risen Jesus would have thrown a brick through the window, and if I have a complaint about Billy Graham, it is that he is too timid.

Billy Graham finished his message a little after nine fifteen last night, and asked everybody to go back to the shop, to the store, to "your situation" and be reborn—"courteous, gracious, kind and loving your neighbor." If anyone would like to come forward and have "the personal encounter with Christ, we're not going to embarrass you; we're not going to ask you to say anything. You know you have to come back to God. Your friends will wait; we won't keep you more than a few minutes." Jacob had to wrestle with the angel, but the bus waits for Billy Graham's disciples.

They came shuffling down from the balconies, by way of the escalators. A few were crying, but none came close to any posture describable as possession. There were great numbers of young people among them; there were also a few of those old women whose faces reminded Baudelaire of old oranges. There was a terrible pathos about them; one thought of the daughter of Lane Adams who told her father, who is one of Billy Graham's team:

"The faces in New York remind me of people who played a game and lost."

They came in docile droves; you remembered the faces of those who had lined up for draft examinations at Governors Island. They seemed an enormous throng. Downstairs, when the heads of the reclaimed—the retreaded really, since an estimated 60 per cent of them already go to church—were tabulated, Lorne Sanney, Billy Graham's Director of Follow-up, estimated that 485 souls had been saved last night.

The rest of this great herd were counselors, advisers, team members, the camp followers commanded by the new science of human behavior to accompany Gideon's army. The counselors were in a permanent state of grace; the recruits had just been through a shattering religious experience; the horror was that you couldn't tell them apart without looking at the badges.

There were 18,500 persons in the Garden last night and 485 of them—less than 3 per cent—had affirmed the experience of the living presence. The figures are below those accounted satisfactory by a direct mail appeal. What was extraordinary was the fact that Billy Graham seemed to feel that this was a triumph of his ministry; he reported that he had never had a better opening, and the records bear him out.

The Clergy

He had stood up downstairs and looked down upon the reborn, looking in the fine condition of the boy whom Babe Ruth, of course, had told once he had the build of a first baseman, and said that his throat was very bad and that he could hardly talk, and that another evangelist would have to deliver the coup. I can only think of this ailment as psychosomatic; he had the letdown that comes to a man who has run his course better than he expected.

It is sad that Billy Graham preaches peace and that the Old Testament God has brought him so little peace. He said in his pre-opening messages all around town early this week that he feared most that God would turn his lips to clay. The sense was inescapable that he was afraid that God might get jealous of his press notices, and punish him for the sin of getting top billing. Last night, at the end, he sounded relieved, as though God had let him off.

He sat on the platform earlier in a terrible paroxysm of the jitters; when he got up to give his message, he went forth with four encouraging slaps on the back from Roger Hull, executive vice president of the Mutual Insurance Co. and chairman of the executive committee of the New York Billy Graham Crusade Inc.

He arose thus fortified and talked for an hour. You watch, because it is your business, for gestures and paces and rhythms and images, but you hope that you will be caught up in them and forget to count; the sad thing is that Billy Graham, as preacher, cannot make you stop counting and begin to inhabit his own world.

He has somehow sterilized the old shouting faith and made it polite, tamed and fit for broken people. The vengeful God is a stallion; in Graham's hands he is a gelding. The references to psychiatry, the call to put away one's tranquilizer pills and go down the escalators to Christ, the quotes from Nathan Pusey, all came out by rote; there was a moment of quiet; the choir began the soft song about going home to Jesus and the terrible interior question came beating forth:

"Is there no more than this, is there no more than this?"

James Gould Cozzens

Pastoral Care

[*Note: Ernest Cudlipp, the Episcopal clergyman, calls on Geraldine, one of his top-drawer parishioners.*]

"Ernie—" she said, strangled.

"My dear, how little we'd disagree, if you'd let yourself see things as they are—or were. Evil can't be done in a nice way. In violating your morals you'll certainly outrage your sensibilities. No, you're not ugly and common. That's why you won't look at it. This great-love business takes two. As far as John's concerned, you can see what it amounts to. He's sick of it. I daresay he has been for a long while. He couldn't have the experience to know what he was letting himself in for. I'm sure you've taught him a lot. Another time—"

She put both hands over her face, dropped her head down to the table. "Come, come!" Ernest said. "Sit up. I won't allow you to start that. You had your emotional spree this afternoon. I don't condemn you, Geraldine; but don't imagine I'm here to condole with you. I want you contrite, not bawling over lost candy. You don't mean to tell me that you don't know how John finally got out from under?"

She sat up; she brought her hands down. With her eyes still shut, she said, "I know. I just couldn't seem to believe it. I knew the last night he was up here. Oh, God, Ernie, it was so awful. I knew he wasn't just tight. He kept saying: 'This is terrible. This is terrible!' But he wouldn't tell me what. He'd say—'Who is she? What's she like?' "

"I don't know. I've only seen her once, at a distance."

"He hasn't been having an affair with her, has he? He couldn't be! He couldn't—"

Ernest sighed. "I don't know that he is; but of course he could. If he isn't, it's because she won't let him. You don't support the finer feelings long when you do without principles. He's a sentimentalist, so he probably finds it all very sad and moving—and unpleasant. But he doesn't stop it. None of them does. That's enough of that. Worry about your own behavior, not his. Where are the children?"

"At my sister's."

"Telephone her and tell her you're coming there. I haven't any idea what the exact situation is with your husband. What does he think you've been doing—or does he know?"

"He's in Cincinnati. I told him I didn't think I was coming back to him, he'd have to let me alone while I—"

"Then write him. Tell him that now you think you are. If he will start again and try to make a go of it, you will."

"I can't."

"You can. Get out of this mess. Go back home and behave yourself. That's easy enough. There isn't anything here for you." He held up the vial of veronal. "When all you can think of is this, what do you call it? Peace and pleasure?"

"Ernie, I would if I could. Why don't you believe me. I can't!"

"Geraldine, what is this nonsense?" He looked at the veronal tablets a moment, speculative. "Haven't you been frank with me? I asked you what was wrong with your husband. When you answer, nothing, I assume that you are telling the truth. This isn't the moment for reticences of that kind. What is he? Habitually unfaithful? Diseased? Impotent? Perverted?"

"Oh," she said. "No! No!" She looked at him a moment, her eyes wide, blank and despairing. "I suppose I have to tell you," she said. "It seems so silly. You see, I couldn't, I really couldn't. Ernie, I'm a couple of months pregnant."

38

Ernest dropped his hands and looked back at her. "Geraldine," he said, shaking his head, "Geraldine. Why did you let that happen?"

"It's silly, isn't it? That's just what I did. I suppose I didn't care. I loved John. I—"

Ernest pressed his palms to his forehead, slid them up, over his thin brown hair. "Were you insane, my dear?" he asked. "I suppose you were! You didn't care. You loved John. And so you thought you'd have a child. Geraldine, a child is a human being. Merciful God, must I tell a sensible woman that? When you undertake to have one, you embark on a business of the greatest seriousness and importance, lasting perhaps twenty years. What on earth am I going to do with you?"

He found a new cigarette slowly, lit it, slouched back in the chair. He put a hand over his eyes and said, "I'll have to think. I'll have to think."

At last he said, "No. Definitely no!" He dropped his hand, crushed the barely begun cigarette out in the ashtray on the table. "Now, let me see what we can do. How about your sister? Would she know—Wait. We can do better than that. Where is the telephone?"

In the darkness of the entry he put his back to the wall. "Lily?" he said. "Mr. Cudlipp. I want to speak to Mrs. Breen, the lady upstairs. Tell her she can take it on that telephone in the back room."

There was a prolonged pause and Lily said suddenly: "She's playing on the piano, Mr. Cudlipp. She don't hear me."

"Now, Lily, go upstairs at once and make her hear you. If those stairs are getting too hard for you to climb, do you know what I'm going to have to do? I'm going to have to get a new housekeeper."

"I'm going, Mr. Cudlipp, as fast as I can—"

After a while a receiver clicked and Alice said, "Ernie, don't you dare tell me you can't get back."

"I'll be along. Listen carefully. Do you know of a decent and capable doctor who will take a case for me?"

"What kind of a case?"

"Try not to be dense, my dear. When I ask you for such information, what kind of a case would you imagine?"

"Oh! Yes. Of course, Ernie. I know a very good one."

"Well, please call him right away and make sure he's in town. I want an appointment for tomorrow."

"She, darling. She. I know she's in town. I was there this afternoon. Not the same thing, though. A funny old man put his head in while I was playing the piano, started to say something, and then ran away as fast as he could. Do you suppose he was a burglar?"

"I suppose he was Mr. Johnston. He's a clergyman who assists me."

"Oh. I'd thought he might be the janitor. Lily's more remarkable than ever, isn't she? I expect I'd fire her."

"She is an extremely good cook."

"Well, it wouldn't hurt her to dust some, sometime. Lee called up, fine and drunk. I think he wanted to apologize to you for missing dinner; but when he found it was I, all he did was accuse you of having designs on me. I told him no such luck and to go to hell. Good-by, darling."

Ernest went back into the bare living room. He took the veronal tablets from his pocket, broke the seal, and shook out two of them. "Do you ever take this stuff?" he asked.

Geraldine shook her head. He put one tablet back and laid the other on the table. "Take it now," he said, "and go to bed. Everything's arranged. I'll call you about it in the morning."

"All right. I don't like it, Ernie. I don't think I ought to do it. I know it's silly to feel that way, but—"

"You ought not to have to do it," he said, "if that is what you mean. You have no right to put yourself in a position where you can only choose between evils, instead of between good and evil. But you cannot continue in any course which involves persistent violation of the rights of others." He fixed his steady brown eyes on her and said, "Come here, Geraldine. You've got into this over your head; but we won't let you drown. Kneel down."

She came automatically, knelt awkwardly, her dress catching tight under her knees, and he put a hand on her shoulder to steady her.

When he had occasion to use one, the long Roman absolution came first to Ernest's mind. It was a relic of seminary days. Spikes like Vincent McNamara and Cael Willever naturally championed it—though there had been a prolonged, enjoyable squabble over the admissibility of the deprecatory form. Thoughtful, Ernest began: "May Almighty God have mercy—"

But it was, he decided, too thick, in view of what Rome would have to say about his directions to her. He turned it into the words of the Prayer Book: "—upon you," he continued, "pardon and deliver you from all your sins, confirm and strengthen you in all goodness, and bring you to everlasting life; through Jesus Christ our Lord . . ."

"Take that tablet," he said.

She put it in her mouth, her face contracting bitterly, and gulped the sherry left in the glass.

"That will take care of you," he said. "Good night, my dear. You're all right. You will be all right."

41

Paris Leary

The Innocent Curate

[*Note: Walter Groby is priest in an Episcopal parish in upstate New York.*]

Mr. Groby, who had driven into town at sixty-five miles per hour, steering with his knees and lighting his pipe with his hands, was something of a shock at first. He had concentrated his attention on the National Electric people in the afternoon and the First Ward at night (the College was left to curates who read books). He courted scientists before dinner and Mrs. Van Rensaaler during and after. He kissed her hand, which, having essayed nothing more difficult than clipping coupons, was still pretty (the rest of Mrs. Van Rensaaler was irretrievably a fat sixty-five). He was a good bridge player, furnished with an inexhaustible treasure of ejaculations appropriate to the spirit of Contract (they all came from Pamela Beauchamp-Fitzwilliams' novels about English country-house life, but no one had ever found out except Mrs. Philip Du-Morey, and she was not believed).

"Not past the iron duchess," he would say, winking at Mrs. Rensaaler when their opponents' finesse failed to work. "*Toujours l'audace!*" before making a difficult play. "May your *sommelier* bring you some refreshments? . . ." Or "Isn't this a charming party, so *ébouillant*, so like this lovely lady herself, that it's difficult to say which of them is the most enjoyable?

. . ." Bending over her with salted nuts, her passion, "There's a new family in the parish I think we'd find worth entertaining . . . really quite civilized."

So with Mrs. Van Rensaaler, so with Mrs. Van Der Horn, so with Mrs. C. Lawrence Waverly. As a matter of fact, the old guard had been quite prepared to hate him and met him with their backs up. He was Western, he was young, and there were rumors about his having contracted some liaison with the purveyors of High Church *décor*. The combination was fatal enough. He was also popular with young people, which, if not fatal, was at least suspicious. But he dazzled the old crowd. He charmed the maiden daughters, who began to dream of playing Héloïse to his Abelard (not that their sheltered minds visualized for a minute to what anatomical straits this would have led him). He paid more attention to widows than their husbands had when alive. He made menopause something on the *qui vive* for the idle and aging aunts of the First Ward. It is difficult to dislike someone when you think he is enchanted by you—and every First Ward woman had come to believe that Mr. Groby believed that conversation had died with Madame de Sévigné only to have its rebirth in her. To those few who did openly oppose him (like Mrs. Philip DuMorey—and her daughter Clothilde who, owing to an unfortunate accident at birth, could never hope for marriage anyway), Mrs. Van Rensaaler reacted with a love-me-love-my-dog attitude which caused a grudging acceptance among even his most vocal adversaries. She was stunningly rich.

So the parish had changed. It had been requisite that it change before he reached middle age, for it was to be a show-place to dioceses with empty bishoprics. Mr. Groby had done nothing without careful malice aforethought since childhood. Or, rather, since infancy, for Walter Groby was never a child. He had been a baby, of course, but suddenly, after his infancy, he had been a scheming, sober little man. By the time he was sixteen he had surveyed the world and himself thoroughly. He had discovered that the world was a cruel place if you had neither money nor position. He had discovered that he was not really intelligent, not in the way of men who write books or build financial empires. He looked round the world some more and had decided to become a clergyman . . . what denomination made little difference at first until, as he grew older, he discovered that Nonconformity, no matter how wealthy, was destined to remain forever on the outside of those who were in. So he became an Episcopalian and set about becoming a bishop. There had been some nonsense at the psychological examination which Canon Law required of all postulants; some idiot psychologist said that he had seen too many cold-blooded reptiles in his Rorschach test—that did not deter him, however. He knew that clergy were paid for doing very little. And he wanted to be a clergyman. He was willing to put up with presbyteral orders for a time, until he should become a bishop. Then he would sit back behind a large desk and dictate letters, preside over meetings, and tell the world to go to hell by preaching heaven at it on his own terms.

He had been willing to give the energies of his youth, to expend himself over St. Clement's, to assure himself of the crown of reward which awaited him. He had always been one of those men who, no matter how young, look forward to a comfortable middle age and are willing to work for it. Though he knew he was not intelligent, he knew that he could get people to do what he wanted by smiling at them, and what other men had sown he knew he could reap. He had one drive which impelled him—the desire for a bishop's mitre. He had no sex drive to speak of, no interest in God, His Son, His Mother, or the common lot of suffering humanity (he talked a lot in his sermons about humanity in their *"souffrance,"* but his French was so bad and he was obviously so delighted with his apprehension of it that the effect was always quite smart).

He had courted the First Ward to get money to attract the N. E. crowd, and in his success with N. E. he had hoped to reach the ears of churchly magazines who record such rectoral feats on glossy pages. He pictured himself handing over N. E., as it were, to God, who, being widely known for generosity, would surely place over his black curls the mitre of an elegant

44

Eastern diocese (sometimes he shuddered to think what he would do if, before God got round to this act, some ghastly diocese, somewhere like Utah or Nebraska, should offer him an episcopal throne—he knew how hardly the words "*Nolo episcopari*" should issue from his lips).

Soon young married couples with children began to swarm about the church on Sunday mornings and Holy Days of Obligation (of which latter there seemed so many more than in Mr. Loth's day . . . you may be sure Mrs. Philip DuMorey made the most of *that*); earnest young men came genuflecting up from the plant to confess publicly that Science and Religion had been knit together by Mr. Groby's skillful hands. Advertising and Sales Promotion were led by Stu Gottwald, like Clovis, to baptism *en masse*. An additional Mass had to be instituted, the Family Mass at nine in the morning—old Schinderhook would have as soon thought of going to church at nine in the morning as it would of making love at half past three on a weekday afternoon and was, besides, more disposed to Matins than to the Body and Blood of their Saviour. But the Family Mass became the main service of the day.

"Every Sunday looks like Easter now," Mr. Groby would say to Mrs. Van Rensaaler, several years after his entrance into Schinderhook, "and so much of the growth is due to you and your generosity."

She had found that she rather enjoyed being Constantine to this new religion. *Licet*, she said at the Upper Club, and no one rebuked Caesar. She bought Mr. Groby five copes in Bruges and an honorary doctor's degree from Teabury–Southern Seminary (his own seminary, St. Dismas' in New York, refused any sum, even a blank check, to grant him such a degree, but there was an indigent seminary in Arkansas which was not so squeamish). From that moment social downfall could be predicated on a failure to address him as "*Doctor* Groby."

Her friends, particularly those who were not Church, watched with some interest to see if her newly activated participation in affairs spiritual would interrupt the love affair she had been having with John Van Briinker for the last forty years. The gentleman in question, President of United Hand-Car Corporation in Schinderhook, had been fool enough to marry a southerner when everyone knew that Fleming Van Rensaaler would be dead of his cancer in a matter of months anyway. After a few years he gave his pansy-eyed wife a million dollars and sent her to Europe to stay. Occasionally she asked him for another million, which she always got. But Mrs. Van Rensaaler's relationship with John Van Briinker, though naturally past its chemical stages, was too much a part of her life, and since St. Margaret's Guild met in the mornings, nothing at St. Clement's ever interfered with it.

As time had gone on, Dr. Groby found himself in other Schinderhook drawing rooms. He dined with Bill and Janice Jenkins, a young couple from Idaho. It was becoming difficult to keep Old Schinderhook and N. E. people separate now, since under his skillful management the two were being slowly blended—and after only seven years. The Jenkinses had three babies. Somehow Old Schinderhook never seemed to have babies, not even the younger set in the First Ward. They all had children at Groton or Skidmore, at Northfield, or St. Agnes' in Albany, but the years between birth and finishing school were the hidden years. Sometimes it had seemed that First Ward children were born at prep-school age.

Not so with the young married set at National Electric. Babies were in evidence everywhere: crying, spilling anonymous brown foods on their chairs and bibs, suddenly nauseated during the sermon, throwing a tantrum when one had a touchy parent all but under the Bishop's confirming hands . . . babies were always in evidence. And their parents, used to the madness, seemed relatively unconcerned, as they waited for one to continue his little explanation of the non-papal character of early British Christianity, that their eldest had just made water on the left clerical trouser leg. People in the First Ward were more careful of spaniels.

But Dr. Groby had managed these things gracefully. Time was passing, and there was work to be done before some committee on episcopal elections should survey St. Clement's and exclaim to him, "Well done, thou good and faithful servant, enter into thy reward . . . be Bishop of Massachusetts." So St. Clement's had become a place of penitent agnostics, reformed scientists, and praying engineers; a place where the sophisticated found such sophistication about religion that they confessed themselves spiritual rubes; where society people found they could be social about piety with sacerdotal approval; and where the ever-growing number of zealous converts to Grobyism could exercise by snubs and economic boycott their zeal on unrepentant and stiff-necked Low Churchmen who still came to church at eleven o'clock and didn't know the Blessed Sacrament from peach pie. . . .

Michael Frayn

Bishop Rock

I believe the readiness of leading churchmen and leading entertainers to discuss religion together on television indicates something of a religious revival. Take the immensely inspiring clash of tenet and dogma that occurred over the weekend, when Rock Richmond, the popular rock 'n' roll singer, met the Bishop of Twicester, the popular press 'n' telly ecclesiast, for a ten-minute discussion ranging over the whole religious field.

Twicester: Let me say first of all, Rock, how very pleased I am to have this chance of a quiet chat together. As you probably know from my press releases, I'm a great fan of yours. My wife and I have often rolled back the carpet after the day's episcopal business and enjoyed a jolly good rock together to one of your recordings. And I can tell you, Rock, that for rocking in, gaiters are every bit as good as drainpipe trousers!

Richmond: Well, I think you're wonderful, too. Whenever I've seen your picture in the paper or on TV I've always thought: Now there's a wonderful man. If only they had more people like him in the Church, they could get the sort of publicity they need. I really mean it.

Twicester: That's very nice of you, Rock. Now, Rock, I'm very glad of this meeting, because I think it's terribly important today for the Church to have a chance to put itself across to young people like yourself, and to tell them exactly what religion is all about. Many young people, I know, feel that religion is just a sort of boring thing to do on Sunday. But it's not like that at all, you see.

Richmond: That's right. There are a lot of kids around today who aren't interested in anything. Now I'm not like that. I think about things.

Twicester: Because when you get down to it, Rock, religion's got nothing to do with going to church on Sunday at all really. You see, religion's not just a narrow set of do's and don'ts, or a lot of abstract doctrine and long-winded ritual. It's your whole way of life. It's—well, it's taking a girl to the pictures. It's doing the town on your motorbike. It's rocking and rolling.

Richmond: I mean, I wouldn't call myself religious or anything. But there's something sort of inside you, isn't there? I mean, where did we come from? Tell me that. There's got to be some sort of explanation, hasn't there?

Twicester: Yes, Rock, religion's doing all the things a young teen-ager like yourself does. In a sense, you see, you're religious whether you want to be or not. I think we in the Church have to realize that the narrow-minded sectarian view of religion just won't wash with the young people of today. We have to make sure that the religion we preach is broad enough to recognize that songs like your "The China Doll I Worship" are really acts of witness to a genuine faith.

Richmond: I mean, just take one example. Take the moon. That didn't get there by accident, did it? There's got to be something to explain it, like, hasn't there? The way I see it, something must have sort of put it there. That's what I call religion.

Twicester: So you see, Rock, if rock 'n' roll and sharing a Coca-Cola with your best girl are all part of religion anyway, young people might just as well do it in church youth clubs, where we can see they don't get into trouble, where we can give them a helping hand to settle down quietly to a useful job

49

and find a nice little wife and a nice little home. And if your songs, like "I'm Cryin' for a Doll to Call My Own" help in this, then you're doing a grand job of work.

Richmond: Yes, well, I wouldn't call myself religious, like, but I think there must be more to this world than meets the eye. I mean, that's religion, isn't it?—Something going on somewhere, but we don't know what.

Twicester: Well, I've enjoyed the chat, Rock. I think I've seen something of your point of view, and I hope you've begun to grasp what I'm driving at. And I hope we've at least managed to show that on fundamental matters the Church and the entertainment industry have something in common.

J. F. Powers

The Prince of Darkness

He slowed down and executed a sweeping turn into the parking lot reserved for patrons of the hamburger. He honked his horn his way, three shorts and a long—victory. She would see his car or know his honk and bring out two hamburgers, medium well, onions, pickle, relish, tomato, catsup—his way.

She came out now, carrying an umbrella, holding it ostensibly more over the hamburgers than herself. He took the tray from her. She waited dumbly, her eyes at a level with his collar.

"What's to drink?"

"We got pop, milk, coffee . . ." Here she faltered, as he knew she would, washing her hands of what recurrent revelation, rather than experience, told her was to follow.

"A nice cold bottle of beer." Delivered of the fatal words, Father Burner bit into the smoking hamburger. The woman turned sorrowfully away. He put her down again for native Protestant stock.

When she returned, sheltering the bottle under the umbrella, Father Burner had to smile at her not letting pious scruples interfere with business, another fruit of the so-called Reformation. Watch that smile, he warned himself, or she'll take it for carnal. He received the bottle from her hands. For all his familiarity with the type, he was uneasy. Her lowered eyes informed him of his guilt.

Was he immoderate? Who on earth could say? *In dubiis libertas*, not?

He recalled his first church supper at Saint Patrick's, a mother bringing her child to the Dean's table. She's going to be confirmed next month, Monsignor. Indeed? Then tell me, young lady, what are the seven capital sins? Pride, Covetousness . . . Lust, Anger. Uh. The child's mother, one of those tough Irish females built like a robin, worried to death, lips silently forming the other sins for her daughter. Go ahead, dear. Envy. Proceed, child. Yes, Monsignor. Uh . . . Sloth. To be sure. That's six. One more. And . . . uh. Fear of the Lord, perhaps? Meekness? Hey, Monsignor, ain't them the Divine Counsels? The Dean, smiling, looking at Father Burner's plate, covered with chicken bones, at his stomach, fighting the vest, and for a second into the child's eyes, slipping her the seventh sin. *Gluttony*, Monsignor! The Dean gave her a coin for her trouble and she stood awkwardly in front of Father Burner, lingering, twisting her gaze from his plate to his stomach, to his eyes, finally quacking, Oh Fawther!

Now he began to brood upon his failure as a priest. There was no sense in applying the consolations of an anchorite to himself. He wanted to know one thing: when would he get a parish? When would he make the great metamorphosis from assistant to pastor, from mouse to rat, as the saying went? He was forty-three, four times transferred, seventeen years an ordained priest, a curate yet and only. He was the only one of his class still without a parish. The only one . . . and in his pocket, three days unopened, was another letter from his mother, kept waiting all these years, who was to have been his housekeeper. He could not bear to warm up her expectations again.

Be a chaplain? That would take him away from it all and there was the possibility of meeting a remote and glorious death carrying the Holy Eucharist to a dying soldier. It would

take something like that to make him come out even, but then
that, too, he knew in a corner of his heart, would be only
exterior justification for him, a last bid for public approbation,
a short cut to nothing. And the chaplain's job, it was whis-
pered, could be an ordeal both ignominious and tragic. It
would be just his luck to draw an assignment in a rehabilitation
center, racking pool balls and repairing ping-pong bats for the
boys—the apostolic game-room attendant and toastmaster.
Sure, Sarge, I'll lay you even money the Sox make it three
straight in Philly and spot you a run a game to boot. You win,
I lose a carton of Chesters—I win, you go to Mass every day
for a week! Hard-headed holiness . . .

There was the painful matter of the appointment to Saint
Patrick's. The Dean, an irremovable pastor, and the Archbishop had argued over funds and the cemetery association.
And the Archbishop, losing though he won, took his revenge,
it was rumored, by appointing Father Burner as the Dean's
assistant. It was their second encounter. In the first days of his
succession, the Archbishop heard that the Dean always said a
green Mass on Saint Patrick's Day, thus setting the rubrics at
nought. Furious, he summoned the Dean into his presence, but
stymied by the total strangeness of him and his great age, he
had talked of something else. The Dean took a different view
of his narrow escape, which is what the chancery office gossips
called it, and now every year, on repeating the error, he would
say to the uneasy nuns, "Sure and nobody ever crashed the
gates of hell for the wearing of the green." (Otherwise it was
not often he did something to delight the hearts of the professional Irish.)

In the Dean's presence Father Burner often had the sensation
of confusion, a feeling that someone besides them stood listening in the room. To free himself he would say things he
neither meant nor believed. The Dean would take the other
side and then . . . there they were again. The Dean's position
in these bouts was roughly that of the old saints famous for
their faculty of smelling sins and Father Burner played the role
of the one smelled. It was no contest. If the Archbishop could

53

find no words for the Dean there was nothing he might do. He might continue to peck away at a few stray foibles behind the Dean's back. He might point out how familiar the Dean was with the Protestant clergy about town. He did. It suited his occasional orthodoxy (reserved mostly to confound his critics and others much worse, like Quinlan, whom he suspected of having him under observation for humorous purposes) to disapprove of all such questionable ties, as though the Dean were entertaining heresy, or at least felt kindly toward this new "interfaith" nonsense so dear to the reformed Jews and fresh-water sects. It was very small game, however. And the merest brush with the Dean might bring any one of a hundred embarrassing occasions back to life, and it was easy for him to burn all over again.

When he got his darkroom rigged up in the rectory the Dean had come snooping around and inquired without staying for an answer if the making of tintypes demanded that a man shun the light to the extent Father Burner appeared to. Now and again, hearkening back to this episode, the Dean referred to him as the Prince of Darkness. It did not end there. The title caught on all over the diocese. It was not the only one he had.

. . . The mark of the true priest was heavy on the Dean. The mark was on Quinlan; it was on Keefe. It was on every priest he could think of, including a few on the bum, and his good friend and bad companion, Father Desmond. But it was not on him, not properly. They, the others, were stained with it beyond all disguise or disfigurement—indelibly, as indeed Holy Orders by its sacramental nature must stain, for keeps, in this world and the one to come. "Thou art a priest forever." With him, however, it was something else and less, a mask or badge which he could and did remove at will, a temporal part to be played, almost only a doctor's or lawyer's. They, the others, would be lost in any persecution. The mark would doom them. But he, if that *dies irae* ever came—and it was every plump seminarian's apple-cheeked dream—could pass as the most harmless and useful of humans, a mail-man, a bus

54

rider, a husband. But would he? No. They would see. I, he would say, appearing unsought before the judging rabble, am a priest, of the order of Melchizedech. Take me. I am ready. *Deo gratias.*

". . . and for your penance say five Our Fathers and five Hail Marys and pray for my intention. And now make a good act of contrition. *Misereatur tui omnipotens Deus dimissis peccatis tuis . . .*" Father Burner swept out into the current of the prayer, stroking strongly in Latin, while the penitent, a miserable boy coming into puberty, paddled as fast as he could along the shore in English.

Finishing first, Father Burner waited for the boy to conclude. When, breathless, he did, Father Burner anointed the air and shot a whisper, "God bless you," kicking the window shut with the heel of his hand, ejecting the boy, an ear of corn shucked clean, into the world again. There was nobody on the other side of the confessional, so Father Burner turned on the signal light. A big spider drowsy in his web, drugged with heat and sins, he sat waiting for the next one to be hurled into his presence by guilt ruddy ripe, as with the boy, or, as with the old ladies who come early and try to stay late, by the spiritual famine of their lives or simply the desire to tell secrets in the dark.

He held his wrist in such a way as to see the sweat gleaming in the hairs. He looked at his watch. He had been at it since seven and now it was after nine. If there were no more kneeling in his section of the Cathedral at 9:30 he could close up and have a cigarette. He was too weary to read his office, though he had the Little Hours, Vespers, and Compline still to go. It was the last minutes in the confessional that got him— the insensible end of the excursion that begins with so many sinewy sensations and good intentions to look sharp at the landscape. In the last minutes how many priests, would-be surgeons of the soul, ended as blacksmiths, hammering out absolution anyway?

A few of the Cathedral familiars still drifted around the

floor. They were day and night in the shadows praying. Meeting one of them, Father Burner always wanted to get away. There were collectors of priests' blessings in a day when most priests felt ashamed to raise their hands to God outside the ceremonies. Their respect for a priest was fanatic, that of the unworldly, the martyrs, for an emissary of heaven. They were so desperately disposed to death that the manner of dying was their greatest concern. But Father Burner had an idea there were more dull pretenders than saints among them. They inspired no unearthly feelings in him, as true sanctity was supposed to, and he felt it was all right not to like them. They spoke of God, the Blessed Virgin, of miracles, cures, and visitations, as of people and items in the news, which was annoying. The Cathedral, because of its location, described by brokers as exclusive, was not so much frequented by these wretches as it would have been if more convenient to the slums. But nevertheless a few came there, like the diarrheic pigeons, also a scandal to the neighborhood, and would not go away. Father Burner, from his glancing contact with them, had concluded that body odor is the real odor of sanctity.

Through the grating now Father Burner saw the young Vicar General stop a little distance up the aisle and speak to a couple of people who were possible prospects for Father Burner. "Anyone desiring to go to confession should do so at once. In a few minutes the priests will be gone from the confessionals." He crossed to the other side of the Cathedral.

Father Burner did not like to compare his career with the Vicar General's. The Archbishop had taken the Vicar General, a younger man than Father Burner by at least fifteen years, direct from the seminary. After a period of trial as Chancellor, he was raised to his present eminence—for reasons much pondered by the clergy and more difficult to discern than those obviously accounted for by intelligence, appearance, and, post factum, the loyalty consequent upon his selection over many older and possibly abler men. It was a medieval act of preference, a slap in the face to the monsignori, a rebuke to the principle of advancement by years applied elsewhere.

The Vicar General had the quality of inscrutability in an ideal measure. He did not seem at all given to gossip or conspiracy or even to that owlish secrecy peculiar to secretaries and so exasperating to others. He had possibly no enemies and certainly no intimates. In time he would be a bishop unless, as was breathed wherever the Cloth gathered over food and drink, he really was "troubled with sanctity," which might lead to anything else, the cloister or insanity.

At precisely 9:30 Father Burner picked up his breviary and backed out of the stall. But then there was the scuff of a foot and the tap of one of the confessional doors closing and then, to tell him the last penitent was a woman, the scent of apple blossoms. He turned off the light, saying "Damn!" to himself, and sat down again inside. He threw back the partition and led off, "Yes?" He placed his hand alongside his head and listened, looking down into the deeper darkness of his cassock sleeve.

"I . . ."

"Yes?" At the heart of the apple blossoms another scent bloomed: gin and vermouth.

"Bless me, Father, I . . . have sinned."

Father Burner knew this kind. They would always wait until the last moment. How they managed to get themselves into church at all, and then into the confessional, was a mystery. Sometimes liquor thawed them out. This one was evidently young, nubile. He had a feeling it was going to be adultery. He guessed it was up to him to get her under way.

"How long since your last confession?"

"I don't know . . ."

"Have you been away from the Church?"

"Yes."

"Are you married?"

"Yes."

"To a Catholic?"

"No."

"Protestant?"

"No."

"Atheist?"

57

"No—nothing."

"Were you married by a priest?"

"Yes."

"How long ago was that?"

"Four years."

"Any children?"

"No."

"Practice birth control?"

"Yes, sometimes."

"Don't you know it's a crime against nature and the Church forbids it?"

"Yes."

"Don't you know that France fell because of birth control?"

"No."

"Well it did. Was it your husband's fault?"

"You mean—the birth control?"

"Yes."

"Not wholly."

"And you've been away from the Church ever since your marriage?"

"Yes."

"Now you see why the Church is against mixed marriages. All right, go on. What else?"

"I don't know . . ."

"Is that what you came to confess?"

"No. Yes. I'm sorry, I'm afraid that's all."

"Do you have a problem?"

"I think that's all, Father."

"Remember, it is your obligation, and not mine, to examine your conscience. The task of instructing persons with regard to these delicate matters—I refer to the connubial relationship—is not an easy one. Nevertheless, since there is a grave obligation imposed by God, it cannot be shirked. If you have a problem . . ."

"I don't have a *problem*."

"Remember, God never commands what is impossible and so if you make use of the sacraments regularly you have every

58

reason to be confident that you will be able to overcome this evil successfully, with His help. I hope this is all clear to you."

"All clear."

"Then if you are heartily sorry for your sins, for your penance say the rosary daily for one week and remember it is the law of the Church that you attend Mass on Sundays and holy days and receive the sacraments at least once a year. It's better to receive them often. Ask your pastor about birth control if it's still not clear to you. Or read a Catholic book on the subject. And now make a good act of contrition. . . ."

Max Wylie

Intercession

[*Note: The scene occurs at the church service led by the Rev. Iverson. Gil is his son.*]

Suddenly the music grew dramatically faint and the three lady trumpeters, at the exact instant when Mr. Hennessy's head went sharply back (which Gil and Jared could always see in the mirror no matter how many flowers the Ladies Decoration had brought), played the last note, lowered their silver horns, and stood still as angels on a postal card, their horns on their hips.

The vestry door opened and Reverend Iverson entered from the left side, the sunlight from the great windows pouring into his tan and eager face as if the brilliance of heaven and Jehovah too were lighting his way to the pulpit. And he walked with his head up, light of step, firm of purpose, smiling and intense and athletic, and carrying the meaning and the spirit and the love of Jesus Christ to all the poor sinners of Scioto County. He walked like a man marching, his eyes on a flag.

"Eyes on the rafters," Mr. Willis had told some of the men at the firehouse, after his first and only experience with Presbyterians. "Lookin' heaven right in the face. If anybody'd left a prayer stool on the platform, Bodie Iverson woulda gone flat on his ass!"

Max Wylie: *Intercession*

Everybody knew that the young minister had been shot at, and his entrance brought a theatrical shimmer to the air above his congregation. There was a light murmur of moiré, a rustle of taffeta, a flicker of aigrettes, hatpins, ladies' watches, birds' wings. And there was a fine, formal smell of shoe polish. It was obvious that many men from the University had come.

The hymns were delightful that morning. On Children's Sunday, the children were allowed to select their own favorite hymns and they did this in Sunday School class the week before. "Crown Him, Crown Him, All Ye Little Children," and "Bringing In The Sheaves" were the first two. And Mr. Hennessy swayed back and forth—you could see the corner of his shoulder—as if he had a pitchfork in his hand and was helping with the sheaves.

It was time for Offertory and Mrs. Stevenson was going to sing "Beulah Land." She sang it better than Miss Killian had done. Miss Killian used to sing alto and her left eye drooped down. Miss Killian got no compliments at all about her singing and one day left Preston without saying good-bye to anyone and married a man in the steel business.

Gilson thought of these things, enjoying the spirit of Mrs. Stevenson, but dreading the long prayer that would follow.

His father began by praying for William Howard Taft who was the President of the United States. He seemed to want to improve him.

"God, give him guidance and courage in these days of strife and tribulation. Give him a greater measure of wisdom than has been his endowment in these recent months of nobility-in-purpose-but-futility-in-accomplishment. Restore to him the probity of mind that promised such full employment, for the welfare of this great nation and its ascending leadership in the world of commerce and affairs. . . . Vouchsafe to him the courage of his own convictions and that ductility of political instinct that gets things done despite the obstruction of the minions of greed and shady principle."

His rich voice rose and fell—now caressing, now lacerating—but always interesting, always picture-provoking, always reminding God to keep busy and to take care of first things first.

He thanked God for sending us men like Jerome K. Jerome and for a Christian imagination that could bring to the theaters of America *The Passing of the Third Floor Back* when the minds of our youth were being drowned in the lewdness of "September Morn," when the women of our land were given the ignoble example of cigarette smoking by "a woman who should use her great influence for the public good—or use it not at all, Mrs. Alice Longworth." He damned Standard Oil and the Tobacco Trust, blessed the *Mauretania* and blessed the keel of the new *Titanic*, but reminded his congregation—and God, too—that while these were majestic symbols of man's ingenuity and his enterprise, there was always, among the rich and the powerful, the temptation to divert their uses to monopoly.

Then he suggested that the United States ought to go after some of the Atlantic trade.

Gil's mind warped away from his father's rich recitals and febrile exhortations. He wished his father would talk a little more about the *Mauretania* but he had begun to pray for the president of Harvard, a man called Lowell, and a man named Hibben who seemed to be the president of some other university that sounded like Preston, only it could not be Preston since Dr. Schermerhorn was the president and was in Beeson Memorial right that minute with the hives.

He opened his eyes cautiously and peeked out at the sea of bowed heads. All the little babies were quiet, most of them asleep. Gil wished one of them would start to cry. This always brought his father's prayers to a faster close, but there was no sound save the voice of the bright tall man in the black robe, and the gold cross swaying, swaying; and the hands open before the Lord, admitting all, but seeming to demand quite a good deal of Him at the same time. Gil felt he could not talk to the Lord in just this same way without the risk of being smitten by one of the scourges of the Old Testament, lightning or leprosy or The Flood.

He'd seen the picture many times, always accompanied by the Avenging Angel with the sword. You could never tell whether it was a Man or a Woman (Jared had told him angels never had to "go" and had nothing there, "Nothing at all"), but there were always dead babies at the bottom and grown-ups screaming and the rain coming down. Gil was careful how he spoke to the Lord when he prayed before going to bed, and never asked for much.

His eye wandered cautiously to the right to see if there were any newcomers but all he could recognize was the back of Mrs. Aikman's head. Then she turned her head very slightly toward Gil's direction and slipped a lozenge into her mouth. Probably a Jujube, Gil thought, for he remembered seeing a box of them in her pocketbook when she had opened it to get a handkerchief. It had been the most recent time that the Thursday Dorcas took place at the Manse, and Gilson had been standing directly in front of her, passing the nut bread.

Mrs. Aikman interested Gil because she seemed to have less reason to complain than even Mrs. Saunders had. Mr. Aikman was known as a great josher but Mrs. Aikman was one who did not care for joshing, at least got sick of it the very minute she got married, so he'd heard. Then Harriet Aikman, who was allowed to do what she pleased as far as Mr. Aikman was concerned but whose mother refused to let her do anything at all—even play tennis or go to the Saturday ball games—ran away from home and joined the Harvey Line of the Santa Fe when she was seventeen. And when her mother found out, four years later, that Harriet had met a man in Colorado Springs and married him, she refused to write her daughter a letter asking for a snapshot of this man. Then when Mr. Aikman heard from Harriet and told his wife that Harriet had a fine son and that the husband seemed to be perfectly all right and was now the boss of the clutch department of the White Automobile Company in Cleveland and took Harriet to Euclid Beach every two weeks to see the balloon ascension and never touched a drop, Mrs. Aikman became so furious that she said she never wanted to see Harriet again, nor her son-in-law, nor her grandchild.

Gil didn't know why the older people could go on being so mean to each other, or to the younger ones—especially when they were for the most part so unpleasant to look at.

Everything about grownups was strange. It had always seemed strange to him that the women of Preston did not seem to pay any attention to the children who might wander in and out of the rooms of the home of almost anybody at all but would just go right on talking and dressing and undressing. He had been playing with Harold Aikman after the Crowfoot twins' birthday party when he and Harold were in first grade and they'd gone to Mr. and Mrs. Aikman's bedroom to get a paper of pins and run right into both Mr. and Mrs. Aikman. Mr. Aikman was looking into the backyard, fanning himself with an almanac, and Mrs. Aikman was sitting on a little stool in front of a tall mirror and cutting off a corn with a razor blade. She did not even notice the boys, just went right on talking to her husband who had the strange first name of Passover.

She had no clothes on whatever and was sitting on a pink bath towel and to Gil's amazement and everlasting curiosity she had a chest just as hairy as any man you ever saw swimming in the Scioto Canoe Club on the days when wives were not allowed and the men took their jerseys off. He could smell earwax and lilac water. It made him a little ill and the recollection of it always made his head ache.

A snap of thunder, tentative but near-by, turned many heads, including Gil's, surreptitiously to the high windows. The rate of his father's praying picked up at once—he hated all kinds of interference—and he quickly prayed for Teddy Roosevelt, Charles Evans Hughes, "my friend and the nation's friend Elihu Root," William Loeb, Pershing, Andrew Carnegie, Billy Sunday, Samuel Gompers, Homer Rodeheaver, and Clara Barton who was said to be sinking.

To Gil it seemed that an unusual number of people were certainly in a lot of trouble.

E. L. Mascall

The Ultra-Catholic

I am an Ultra-Catholic—No 'Anglo-', I beseech
you!
You'll find no trace of heresy in anything I teach
you.
The clergyman across the road has whiskers and
a bowler,
But I wear buckles on my shoes and sport a
feriola.

My alb is edged with deepest lace, spread over
rich black satin;
The Psalms of David I recite in heaven's own
native Latin,
And though I don't quite *understand* those awkward moods and tenses,
My *ordo recitandi's* strict *Westmonasteriensis.*

I teach the children in my school the Penny
Catechism,
Explaining how the C. of E.'s in heresy and
schism.
The truth of Trent and Vatican I bate not one
iota.
I have not met the Rural Dean. I do not pay my
quota.

From *Pi in the High* by E. L. Mascall, copyright © 1959 by The Faith
Press Ltd., London. Reprinted by permission of the publisher.

The Clergy

The Bishop's put me under his 'profoundest dis-
approval'
And, though he cannot bring my actual removal,
He will not come and visit me or take my con-
firmations.
Colonial prelates I employ from far-off mission-
stations.

The music we perform at Mass is Verdi and
Scarlatti.
Assorted females form the choir; I wish they
weren't so catty.
Two flutes, a fiddle and a harp assist them in the
gallery.
The organist left years ago, and so we save his
salary.

We've started a 'Sodality of John of San Fagon-
dez'
Consisting of the five young men who serve High
Mass on Sundays;
And though they simply will not come to week-
day Mass at seven,
They turn out looking wonderful on Sundays at
eleven.

The Holy Father I extol in fervid perorations,
The Cardinals in curia, the Sacred Congregations;
And, though I've not submitted yet, as all my
friends expected,
I should have gone last Tuesday week, had not
my wife objected.

Peter Malton

Matrimonial Causes and Reconciliation Bill

Dear Vicar, will you, or the curate
Come home with me now please, to bed.
My husband and I've been long parted
And I very much now want to wed.
I thought that this Bill in the Commons,
The one about mutual consent,
Would make a long, sad separation
An obvious proof of intent
That we neither can live any longer
As husband and wife. But I find
That the Churches protest at the Measure
And insist that the corporate mind
Of the country, though pagan, be Christian,
And all must obey a decree
Which admittedly seems right for Christians,
But not for non-Christians like me.
Since you do not allow this solution
To a fact, which though tragic is true,
Divorce through the usual channels
Is all I'm permitted to do.
Since you think this is better I'll have to
(Is that what adultery's for?)
And encourage a man to my bedroom
And enjoy a short time as a whore.
Since I can't find a man who is willing
To fulfill these requirements of law

From *Prism Magazine* (London), August 1963. Reprinted by permission of Prism Publications, Limited, London.

The Clergy

I come to you, sir, with this problem
And ask for your help with this chore.
Since you are the source of the trouble,
If it's truly implied what I've said,
Dear Vicar, will you, or the curate
Come home with me now, please, to bed.

Gregory Wilson

The Stained Glass Jungle

[*Note: Jack Winters, young Methodist minister, and his older colleague, Wes Philips, battle the ecclesiastical Tammany Hall led by the District Superintendent, Dr. Worthington, alias "The Beloved".*]

"I've decided you're right," Jack said. "Dr. Worthington does deserve to boss the rest of us. He's fair, he's informed, he loves the church, and he works twice as hard as anyone else!"

"Those are not his only advantages," Wes replied, as if thinking aloud. "His biggest advantage is actually moral. He may very well be the only minister in this conference who can deliberately, consciously, and even systematically do wrong whenever he feels it is necessary. To hold an organization in line year after year, to keep it unified in policy and program, and to override the variety of individual consciences that ministers display, you've got to be able to pray with one man, preach at the next, and kick the third in the teeth. And be smart enough to know what goes with whom.

"I can scarcely imagine Dr. Worthington kicking anyone in the teeth," said Jack, smiling.

"No," said Wes, "because you couldn't do it yourself, and neither could most of the rest of us. You couldn't have forced Oscar Bates to retire at fifty-nine when older men than he were producing less. But your attitude toward Beloved may also be a tribute to his own powers of self-deception. He certainly finds punitive actions intensely painful, and he's probably sincere in imagining they're always just 'disciplinary.' He doesn't seem aware of the strength of his own ambition and love of power, but I guess most ministers never are. Isn't it strange that if a man tramples on his wife and children and betrays his conscience and crucifies his self-respect trying to be president of a button factory, we call it sin. But if a preacher does all the same things trying to make it to the First Church, we admire the monster and have our kiddies pray for him!"

"I'm sure," he went on, "that Beloved agonizes in prayer over the tough things he sometimes has to do to stay in power; but when he gets up from his knees, he can strike hard and forget it. He's not crippled by any glimpses of his own ability to make mistakes. His strength never seems divided by any suspicion that the will of God could be different from his own. He honestly believes he is only what he seems to himself and to you—a mild, hard-working, harmless little country parson whose one aim in life is to build up the church to the glory of God.

"But by long experience, the men have learned that he'll treat you fair if he possibly can; he'll punish you if he must; and if you come back a second time, he'll crucify you."

Jack stared at the old man's cracked shoes, his shiny suit, frayed cuffs, and unkempt white hair.

"I can't believe," Jack said, "that almost five hundred Methodist ministers would let themselves live under a reign of terror for twenty-five years without rebelling!"

"It's no reign of terror!" Wes replied. "It's only in the last five or ten years that his power began to be so pervasive; you forget that it took him a long time to build this machine. And he rarely has to threaten anybody. Constructive appeals and reasonably fair rewards for seniority and hard work are all you need in handling most preachers. It's like working in a bank or department store. No body comes around in a black mustache and cracks a whip over you. The boss is a Christian gentleman,

70

and nothing would offend him more than to think people feared him. But the pressure is always there. . . .

"What makes Beloved different is that most ministers cannot admit even to themselves that career and status are almost always their first consideration—plus fear of failure. But he looks the facts square in the eye and uses them for all they're worth!"

"Lots of preachers," Wes said thoughtfully, "have lived under this arrangement all their lives and honestly don't even seem to know it's there! I keep telling Beloved he ought to dress the part. 'Wear a diamond stickpin, Man!' I told him once. 'Look like the bosses in books! Drive a black limousine; smoke a big cigar; hire a couple of thugs to be your bodyguards. Confound it, man, we have two dozen new men coming up for appointment this year, and not a single one of them will know where to turn. Half of them will probably try to see the bishop or some other nobody, and let you walk right past under their noses! Take off that disguise,' I told him, 'and play the part the good Lord gave you!' "

"What did he say?"

"Oh, you know Beloved! He just laughed his merry little laugh and shook his little billiard-ball head, and patted my arm with his warm little hand the way he does, and said, 'Why, Wes, if I tried to smoke a cigar, I'd probably end up in the hospital!' "

He walked down the cinder path to the car with Jack after supper and stood leaning against the gatepost.

"Wes," said Jack curiously, "you seem to agree with your enemy's estimate of human nature. Why have you never joined him?"

"Any fool," said Wes, "can cash in on the weaknesses of his fellow men. I never considered that much of a challenge."

"Well," said Jack, "at least tell me why you haven't transferred to another conference."

"Oh, tarnation, boy! I can't explain my choices to a kid like you! You're of a generation that expects every act to serve some useful purpose."

71

The Clergy

Wes turned half-about, and Jack followed his gaze as it took in the ancient parsonage and the faded white frame church . . . not the kind of house most ministers were willing to live in, not the kind of church that gave scope and effectiveness to a man with this man's gifts. As they watched, Sue Philips appeared briefly on the porch. She was always like Wes— calm, cheerful, undismayed—but Jack knew that for a man as sensitive to others as Wes, the hardships his choices had brought upon Sue and the children must have been a crucifying moral dilemma. By all the currently accepted standards of the ministry, Wes Philips' career was a failure and his gifts wasted, yet Jack had rarely found himself seeking counsel of the men who were successful—the men with the booming suburban churches and the split-level parsonage and the statistical proofs of their prophethood.

"Just what does keep you going?" Jack demanded. "You've been fighting a lost cause now for twenty-five years, and I suppose you were in there battling the old Doffingwell machine before that. Explain yourself, sir!"

The old man closed the rickety gate between them, almost as if he were drawing a line between their generations.

"When I was coming up," said Wes Philips sourly, "a man didn't have to explain a sense of honor."

Part Two:

God and the National Pantheon

Since World War II so much of religion has been homogenized with Americanism that we have lived in a veritable Constantinian dispensation of public prosperity conjoined with piety. In the 1950's the student lounges at many Protestant seminaries witnessed imitations of Norman Vincent Peale sermonizing on the entrepreneurial virtues, while out in the countryside belief in God and the Dow-Jones average soared up together. These were the years when Professor Will Herberg and other sociologists of religion began to write of our pan-confessional establishment—a pluralistic, syncretistic religiosity. All of this naturally was an inviting target for satirists who now had to perform for American society what they had done so often before in history: remind churchman and politician that God is not a precinct worker. The satirist may correct the balance when religion and politics are crudely mixed; but the satirist does not solve the problem. It is never balanced out. It was remarked of Bismarck that he left his religion at home with his breakfast napkin when he departed each morning for the Wilhelmstrasse. That's one extreme. The American politician usually lapses into the other—of wiping his political face with altar cloths in full view of the public.

WILLIAM LEE MILLER's picture of a 1954 version of God–and–Country may seem slightly dated, but it was real enough at the time. A syndrome of a similar sort was, unfortunately, more in evidence after President Kennedy's death, when there broke out one of the worst exhibitions of bathos, cheap art, poor poetry, and tasteless prayers in all our history. It would have grieved the late President, but it surely was post-mortem evidence of the amount of incense burning in the national Capitol. HOWARD NEMEROV's acidic lines on booming religion, with Job in Palestine and Eisenhower at Atlantic City providing the contrast, may be unfair to Ike and brutal on the Rev. Mr. Elson (who was Ike's Washington pastor), but it was salutary in its effect on our national conscience. If satirists paused to be fair, there would be no satire. Proximate justice must serve. The "Pen-ultimate" column in the *Christian Century* closes in on L.B.J.'s priorities of consensus, folksiness, and godliness.

William Lee Miller

Piety Along the Potomac

The manifestations of religion in Washington have become pretty thick. We have had opening prayers, Bible breakfasts, special church services, prayer groups, a "Back to God" crusade, and campaign speeches on "spiritual values"; now we have added a postage stamp, a proposed Constitutional amendment, and a change in the Pledge of Allegiance. The Pledge, which has served well enough in times more pious than ours, has now had its rhythm upset but its anti-Communist spirituality improved by the insertion of the phrase "under God." The Postmaster General has held a dedication ceremony, at which the President and the Secretary of State explained about spiritual values and such, to launch a new red, white, and blue eight-cent postage stamp bearing the motto "In God We Trust." A bill has been introduced directing the post office to cancel mail with the slogan "Pray for Peace." (The devout, in place of daily devotions, can just read what is stuck and stamped all over the letters in their mail.)

The inaugural prayer of the President now hangs under glass on the wall of the Vice-President's office, just as "God Bless Our Home" or the Golden Rule used to hang in other places. After his election, the President joined a church. To one of the many church groups he has met with he said that he prefers his preachers to be vigorous and forthright in defense

From *Piety Along the Potomac* by William Lee Miller, Houghton Mifflin Company, Boston, 1964. Reprinted by permission of the publisher and the author.

75

of their position. (None of the visiting clergymen thought to say that he prefers his Presidents that way too.) Cabinet meetings are now said to be started with prayer. (An irreverent Washington joke ends, "Dammit, we forgot the opening prayer.") *Life* Magazine's article on the President's religion reports an increased attendance at Senate, House, and departental prayer groups. (It also reports the complaint that these groups seem "to enjoy listening to lay speakers who easily equate piety with personal prosperity.") For the Very Big Men there are the annual prayer breakfasts of the International Council of Christian Laymen with grapefruit, scrambled eggs, a New Testament reading by Vice-President Nixon, and the singing of one of the President's favorite hymns, "What a Friend We Have in Jesus."

Elmer Davis wrote about Independence Day a year ago: "The greatest demonstration of the religious character of this administration came on July Fourth, which the President told us all to spend as a day of penance and prayer. Then he himself caught four fish in the morning, played eighteen holes of golf in the afternoon, and spent the evening at the bridge table."

To note all this in a deflationary tone is not to say that religion and politics don't mix. Politicians should develop deeper religious convictions, and religious folk should develop wiser political convictions; both need to relate political duties to religious faith—but not in an unqualified and public way that confuses the absolute and emotional loyalties of religion with the relative and shifting loyalties of politics.

Most of the problems with the public sort of thing are illustrated in the following story from the New York *Times* of January 19, 1953:

> Carpenters raced against time in a remote corner of the National Guard Armory here today to complete an added starter to the procession of floats in Tuesday's Inaugural Parade. To the three men who conceived the idea it is known as "God's Float." They hope it will come to be known as such throughout the world.

William Lee Miller: *Piety Along the Potomac*

> Last week the floats were nearing completion
> in the armory basement. Then it was discovered
> by a parade official that nowhere was there to
> be any representation that this was a nation
> whose people believed in God.
>
> Then, in keeping with the Biblical precept,
> inaugural officials decided that this—the last float
> conceived—should be the first in the order of
> march.
>
> It will have constructed on its base a central
> edifice denoting a place of worship. The side
> aprons will carry greatly enlarged photographs
> of churches and other scenes of worship. In
> Gothic script on the sides and ends of the float
> will appear the legends, "Freedom of Worship"
> and "In God We Trust."

The object of devotion for this float is "religion." The faith
is not in God but in faith; we worship our own worshiping.
The symbols are "greatly enlarged photographs" of "scenes of
worship."

Of the monstrosity which resulted from this particular
effort the *Episcopal Churchnews* wrote: "Remember the float
representing religion in President Eisenhower's inaugural
parade? Standing for all religions, it had the symbols of none,
and it looked like nothing whatsoever in Heaven above, or in
the earth beneath, except possibly an oversized model of a
deformed molar left over from some dental exhibit."

Since this is official religion in a land without an official
religion it cannot be very deep. The careful inoffensiveness of
public office leads straight to the semi-secular religion or the
semi-religious secularism which is both a convenient compromise among the wide variety of positions to which officialdom
must be attentive and a very popular position in its own right.

The content of official religion is bound to be thin; the
commitment to it is also apt to be hollow now and then.
Where everybody professionally believes something, then for
some the belief may be a bit more professional than real. A

float may not represent a faith integral to the participants' lives, but rather the prudent recollection by a functionary of what the public would expect. Religion is now very popular, and the politician's business is to know and to follow what is popular. Letters, according to the *Times* amounting to thousands daily, "flooded Congress" in support of the change in the Pledge. Newspapers (prominent among them the Hearst chain) and radio commentators endorsed it, and organizations like the Knights of Columbus gave it hearty support.

Too often this dubious mixture of patriotism and religion serves the purposes of a conservative social philosophy, as when the old ways in faith bless the old ways in economics. There may be a touch of this blessed conservatism, and there certainly is more than a touch of blessed nationalism, in the American Legion's "Back to God" crusade.

Mr. Nixon, speaking on behalf of it, is apparently convinced, like the Legion, that the direction in which God is to be found is "back." Mr. Nixon's remarks at that time illustrate a constant theme of Washington piety: Promote religion because it is useful to the nation in fighting Communism. He emphasized that the country's greatest asset in fighting Communism is its spiritual heritage. The note of pride and invidious self-congratulation for this "advantage" became very plain in his list of things we have that they do not. "Among the great privileges that we enjoy is the privilege of hearing President Eisenhower pray at the beginning of his inauguration. That could not happen in half the world today. We also have the privilege of attending the churches of our choice. That, too, could not happen in half the world today." Mr. Nixon called free worship "our greatest defense against enemies from without"; Mr. Eisenhower on a radio-TV program launching the crusade called faith "our surest strength, our greatest resource." In his remarks on the Pledge he said, "We shall constantly strengthen those spiritual weapons which forever will be our country's most powerful resource, in peace or in war." This reduction of religion to a national "resource," "advantage," "strength," and "weapon," especially useful for anti-Communist purposes, received perhaps its perfect expression from the perfect folk hero for the devotees of such an outlook, J. Edgar Hoover, when he wrote, "Since Communists are anti-God, encourage your child to be active in the church."

Officialdom prefers religion which is useful for national purposes, but undemanding and uncomplicated in itself. It also wants religion which is negotiable to the widest possible public. Therefore the official faith is easily impressed with the spread of any simple external sign of religion, however empty of content. The President praised the Legion's "Back to God" movement as a "positive act," and he said of the postage stamp that "the sender can feel he has done something positive and constructive." His picture of the result of the addition of two words to the Pledge also seems a little extravagant: "From this day forward, the millions of our school children will daily proclaim in every city and town, every village and rural school house, the dedication of our nation and our people to the Almighty. To anyone who truly loves America, nothing could be more inspiring than to contemplate this rededication of our youth, on each school morning, to our country's true meaning."

But two more words in chorus each morning represent no such dedication, nor does Congress's passing the bill to change the Pledge constitute a dedication; sending a stamp is nothing "constructive," and a big promotion campaign with placards saying "Go to Church" is not an especially "positive act."

All religious affirmations are in danger of standing in contradiction to the life that is lived under them, but none more so than these general, inoffensive, and externalized ones which are put together for public purposes.

What is affirmed often stands in ironic contrast to what is otherwise being done and thought and said.

An old cartoon by Robert Day in the *New Yorker* illustrates what I mean: A street-corner evangelist whose sign reads LOVE THY NEIGHBOR shouts to a competitor, "I'm telling you for the last time—keep the hell off this corner!"

79

Howard Nemerov

Sees Boom in
Religion, Too

*Alantic City, June 23, 1957 (AP).—President
Eisenhower's pastor said tonight that Americans
are living in a period of "unprecedented religious
activity" caused partially by paid vacations, the
eight-hour day and modern conveniences.*

*"These fruits of material progress," said the
Rev. Edward L. R. Elson of the National Presbyterian Church, Washington, "have provided the
leisure, the energy, and the means for a level of
human and spiritual values never before reached."*

Here at the Vespasian-Carlton, it's just one
religious activity after another; the sky
is constantly being crossed by cruciform
airplanes, in which nobody disbelieves
for a second, and the tide, the tide
of spiritual progress and prosperity
miraculously keeps rising, to a level
never before attained. The churches are full,
the beaches are full, and the filling-stations
are full, God's great ocean is full
of paid vacationers praying an eight-hour day
to the human and spiritual values, the fruits,
the leisure, the energy, and the means, Lord,
the means for the level, the unprecedented level,

and the modern conveniences, which also are full.
Never before, O Lord, have the prayers and
   praises
from belfry and phonebooth, from ballpark and
   barbecue
the sacrifices, so endlessly ascended.

It was not thus when Job in Palestine
sat in the dust and cried, cried bitterly;
when Damien kissed the lepers on their wounds
it was not thus; it was not thus
when Francis worked a fourteen-hour day
strictly for the birds; when Dante took
a week's vacation without pay and it rained
part of the time, O Lord, it was not thus.
But now the gears mesh and the tires burn
and the ice chatters in the shaker and the priest
in the pulpit, and Thy Name, O Lord,
is kept before the public, while the fruits
ripen and religion booms and the level rises
and every modern convenience runneth over,
that it may never be with us as it hath been
with Athens and Karnak and Nagasaki,
nor Thy sun for one instant refrain from shining
on the rainbow Buick by the breezeway
or the Chris Craft with the uplift life raft;
that we may continue to be the just folks we are,
plain people with ordinary superliners and
disposable diaperliners, people of the stop 'n' shop
'n' pray as you go, of hotel, motel, boatel,
the humble pilgrims of no deposit no return
and please adjust thy clothing, who will give to
   Thee,
if Thee will keep us going, our annual
Miss Universe, for Thy Name's Sake, Amen.

Dialing Consensus

Yes, Mr. Johnson. Yes, I saw the clipping. Yes, I showed it to all your other aides, too. No, they were delighted. Yes, the wire services really handled this one nicely. No, there weren't any snide comments. Oh, you must have a different version; let me read this one to you. It'll be music to your ears. Yes . . .Yes . . .

Well, in the one I have in front of me it says, "About two weeks after his historic meeting with Pope Paul, Mr. Johnson plans to attend a revival meeting in Houston which will be conducted by Billy Graham. . . ." Oh, this one is better—only 15 words including your name between "Pope Paul" and "Billy Graham." . . . I'm sure they'll all get the point. . . . I know, the WASP's were griping all the way from the Pedernales to 475 Riverside Drive about that pope business—the Billy Graahm tie-in will take care of the Pedernales people. . . . We can find some gimmick to satisfy 475 Riverside Drive. . . . No, I think you did right in promising Billy you'd go to meetin' with him for equal time. . . . I'm sure it was good timing. . . . Sure, it ought to take care of almost everybody. . . .

Yes . . . Yes . . . Yes, I took care of Billy. He promised he'd sandwich in a sermon between the two nightly commercials for his new book the night you're there. . . . Yes, *World*

Aflame. . . . Oh, you'll get a big bang out of it. Heh! Heh!
No, not trying to be sacrilegious . . . just thought you'd enjoy
a little joke on such a grim day. . . . Yes, *World Aflame* tells
you not to bother too much about Vietnam and Berkeley and
Watts—what with all the hanky-panky in high places, one of
these days v–r–o–o–o–m! Armageddon! No, no third term,
then. . . .

Oh, I think you should go, even if the book doesn't make
sense. . . . It's the *sym*bolism of your being there that
matters. . . . Yes, I heard that the Methodists didn't feel
covered by the Pope Paul–Billy Graham combo. . . . We can
drop in on that little Methodist church up at Camp David one
of these weekends. . . . The Lutherans? They're soreheads.
They don't like the pope *or* Billy? Well, we can run that three-
year-old shot of you and those dignitaries at that funny little
Lutheran church in Texas. That went over big last time. . . .

Yes, I agree that having three denominations in your own
family is nice symbolism, too. . . . No, they won't let us
move up Brotherhood Week and make October Brotherhood
Month. . . . Yes, we heard that Mad Murray is mad as hell,
but—honest, chief—how many votes do the atheists have?
. . . Look, some of us are starting to worry a little bit. . . .
All these novenas and masses and prayer breakfasts and church
services and revival meetin's: you hardly have time to run the
country. . . . Oop! I'm sorry, I didn't mean to be telling you
how to run the country—no . . . no . . . only worried
about *when* you'll find time to run the country. . . . Oh,
God, no, don't get mixed up with Churches of God. . . .
There're ten of them, ten different Churches of God denominations in the *Yearbook* . . . and still 240 other denominations to go for consensus . . . can't join 'em all.

Look, Mr. President, wouldn't it save time if you'd just join
the Bahais and be done with it? . . .

Part Three:

The Church Camouflaged

"The Church is the place where man searches for God; it is also the last place where man hides from God." That remark is attributed to Karl Barth, and everyone concerned with corruption in religion should be thankful to him. From Sinai to Malachi, from Herod to St. John, the same point is made: that the God above history, being concerned with history, nevertheless cannot be encapsulated within it. Karl Marx, looking at the way in which the English, German, and Russian churches had tried to engage God, was at least honest enough to know that you can't have it both ways. The satirist may or may not believe in God, but neither will he tolerate the humbug which, whether in suburban Canaan or urban Gomorrah, finds the ritual and faith so blending with the surrounding social ethos that God and man scarcely can be differentiated. In this section the critics lash out at attempts of the church to take on the protective coloration of the world around. The trouble is, however, that we can't have a cultureless religion; short of angelism or docetism, we cannot escape our historical and institutional shadows.

The Church Camouflaged

SHEPHERD MEAD, hep to all the argot of the advertising fraternity ("Let's wrap it up in a big ball of wax" is Madison Ave. talk for launching a completely packaged sales campaign), applies his imagination to a Christian Church which has decided to put consumer ratings above Gospel. PETER DE VRIES has done for suburban religion what Mark Twain did for Missouri Sunday Schools. De Vries, having been reared in an ultra-conservative Calvinistic home, has the advantage of at least knowing a vertebrate theology when he sees it. The Westchester counties of this land are much the better for having been shown how thin and lukewarm and blasphemous are some of the commuter's Sunday rites. LAWRENCE FERLIN-GHETTI's poem about powderblue Christmas trees has been canonized, and it now appears widely in the church press. No one solicitous for the fate of the Christ Child ever did a more herculean job of cleansing the Manger of its Augean junk. JOHN BETJEMAN is surely one of the finest poets in England. He is a leading Anglican—though such a phrase would sound terribly presumptuous to him. He is also the author of delightful books about English church architecture. His poem castigates that dreadfully smug identification of faith with class, with country, and with social status—the cultural lasso once again thrown at the head of God. PETER MALTON contributes a companion piece from within the C. of E., this time about a perfunctory acculturized baptism. Is the Church nothing more than a version of the National Parks, open to the camping of any tourist? JOHN BAINBRIDGE has raucous fun with the way in which the churches, sects, and cults of Texas have set up squatter's rights in God's heaven.

Shepherd Mead

The Big Ball of Wax

[*Note: Lanny, our raconteur, is being shown Your Church by Harry, one of its members.*]

I had to admit it was a nice set-up. There was a tall white steeple with the standard Your Church sign on top.

Y-C FOR YOU AND ME

It was in the standard golden neon and flashed on and off, first just the Y-C, then FOR YOU AND ME, then it all went black and all of it flashed on at once. Below that on the steeple was a really top-quality Momsday* display. It had a Mom in pink-and-blue neon, and it not only rocked back and forth, but the Mom's head kind of bobbed separately. It was very realistic.

"Say, that's real cute," I said.

"Glad you like it," said Harry. "I'm chairman of the Decorations Committee."

The building itself was arena-shaped, like almost all Your Churches. I had to admit this was a practical idea since you didn't have to build two buildings, one for the services and the other for the parish house and the basketball games and all. There was sort of an office-building annex, too.

* By 1992 Momsday (the successor to Mother's day) was the biggest day of the advertising year, next to Christmas.

The Church Camouflaged

We walked in the front way, past the steeple.

"Listen," said Harry, stopping.

I could hear a whispering noise high up in the air.

"That's our Praisegod Machine," said Harry, "an exclusive Your Church development. Actual recordings of the entire congregation. They're doing some real fine hymns and some specially-written Praisegod talk. We had a top script man do it up for us, brought him in from New York. Money was no object. And then, Lanny-boy, get this. We had the whole thing multiple-recorded, every single voice is multipled fifty times. And whatta we do? We play it all the time, twenty-four hours a day. The statistics on it are pretty wonderful. Actually praise-wise we figure forty-eight hours of this equals the entire congregation singing away every Sunday for fifteen years!"

"It should make God very happy, all right."

"We beam it right straight up."

"Why don't you beam it directional?" I asked him.

"Which direction?" said Harry.

"You call the Episcopal Church down the street and they'll tell you."

Harry slapped his thigh.

"Lanny-boy," he said, "you're okay."

This proves once again my point that a little joke, in good taste at the right time, always helps in a business relationship.

"But all kidding aside," said Harry, "this thing saves us one hell of a lot of time which otherwise might be wasted just singing hymns, and all that. We sure can use it, Boy, building up the moral fibers and making contacts, all of which are mighty important in our sensible straight-thinking Your Church policy."

I looked up at the marquee as we walked in. It read:

GIRLS' SOFTBALL TONITE	VIOLETS VS. KIRKWOOD
DOUBLE HEADER	DISH NITE
FRI–SAT SALOME'S MAN	MON NITE BEANO

"The Violets are our team," Harry said. "Last year they were Missouri Valley Y-C Conference Champs. They really

oughta kick the buh-jesus outa Kirkwood tonight. My kid
Kerry is goin' out for shortstop next year."

"That's swell," I said.

"If she's good enough it'll practically put her through
school."

Harry showed a pass to the girl at the change window and
we walked past the turnstiles and into the lobby. I had to
admit it was done in pretty swell taste but yet not stuffy. You
could probably describe it best as a nice combination of hep
and holy. All around the side were Gothic windows maybe
thirty feet high and in each one, rear-projected, was a Coming
Attraction, all done up very cleverly to look kind of like a
stained-glass window, only gutsier. On the FRI–SAT one there
was a really socko picture of Salome in a pose like she was
doing a kind of bump and grind with the head right there on
the platter and SALOME'S MAN in big glitter letters.

"Lotta sock, huh?" said Harry.

"Yeah."

"Believe it or not, it all comes from the central booking in
little slides. The different Y-Cs can fit 'em to any size rear-
projection window. We figure we gotta get the new ones in
movement, though, especially now with the Molly Blood
competition."

All around the walls were pinball machines, about thirty of
them. They were all built in, sort of Gothic, and they blended
in fine with the big windows.

"We got all kinds," said Harry, "Old Testament, New
Testament, and a few just plain Inspiration types. You'd be
surprised, they practically pay for the joint."

At least a dozen of the machines were in use, so I could see
they were doing a nice job sales-wise. You could see the lights
flashing all over.

"Why doncha go over and kill a couple of bucks, Lanny-
boy, while I phone up Will?"

"Okay."

Harry went to a House Vid, and I wandered over to one of
the machines, an Old Testament. There was a gum machine

right next to it and since I saw it had Con Chem gum in it, I dropped a copper quarter in and got a stick. Then I plunked a brass dollar into the pinball machine slot. A dozen balls came out.

I snapped the plunger and sent the first ball shooting up the incline. It hit Samson, Delilah, David, Absalom, and the Queen of Sheba for a score of ten thousand. After six more balls I had seventy-two thousand, and the wall in front of me looked like the Aurora Borealis.

Harry was finished with the Vid. By the time he got over to me I had shot all twelve balls and the whole thing was lit up. It was playing a recording of the "Hallelujah Chorus."

"Well, God dammit," said Harry, "what'd you do?"

"I just kept pulling the plunger."

"Beginner's luck, boy."

Quite a few of the other players were standing around me. "He even lit up the Burning Bush," one guy said.

"Cash it, Lanny-boy, cash it," Harry said, snapping a lever.

"You mean money comes out?"

"What *he* said!" Harry looked at the other players and a couple of them laughed. A card slid out. On one side were the Ten Commandments and on the other a picture of David in a kind of sexy pose with Bathsheba.

"It wouldn't be legal for real money to come out, Lanny-boy," said Harry. He held the card up to the light and whistled. "Forty bucks!" he said.

One of the regular players looked at it closely and said, "Forty-*two*."

I could see then that the card had IBM holes in it.

"I'll cash it for you," Harry said.

The lights in the machine went off, the record stopped, and the other players went away, shaking their heads. An elevator opened and a man came walking out. He was wearing a nice Cashlon tweed suit and a shirt with a low-cut minister's collar. He was about forty, with receding blond hair and a face that looked as though he had scrubbed it with a brush, though he probably hadn't. It was very pink and clean.

"Hi, Harry," he said, "howsa boy?"

"Hi, Will. This is Lanny Martin, Friendly Will Stannard, Lanny. He runs the joint."

We said hi. I guess I don't have to tell any of you that Friendly is what the Your Churches use the way some people use Rev. or Reverend.

*　*　*　*　*

"There he is," said Will, "our Founder, the late Right Friendly Harry Wilker Murray. *He* was a merchandising man and a good one."

"Matter of fact," said Harry, "he was with Con Chem for a while."

"Right," said Will. "A real top merchandising man. Well, sir, one day the Big Idea just sort of appeared to him. He was sitting in church one Sunday and the place was practically empty. In fact, there weren't even enough people around to make any contacts—you know, bulling around on the front steps and all after the service. He said to himself, 'What the U.S.A. needs is a new religion which will get people up off their tails and into church.' So what'd he do?" Will looked at me, hard.

"I don't know."

"What would *you* do if you were launching a new product?"

"I'd make sure it was what people wanted."

"How?"

"I'd run a survey. I'd test the color and the package, and give 'em what most of the people wanted."

"Beautiful, huh, how a merchandising guy thinks?"

"Right," said Harry.

"Well," said Will, "he surveyed the tail off of it, and he found that religion was still in the horse-and-buggy stage. People were hungry for real Comfort, they were hungry for God, boy, but nobody had ever put him in the right package. In your lingo and mine, Lanny, it was a job of damn good package design and marketing know-how. And sales-wise it took off like a goosed rabbit."

91

Peter De Vries

A Mature Faith

Like most irritable people I rarely lose my temper (a dog that's let out for regular exercise isn't as apt to run away when it does escape), but I was losing it this morning. I said into the telephone, "Office of the Zoning Board? This is Mr. Mackerel. Reverend Mackerel—of P. L."

"?"

"People's Liberal."

"Oh, yes. That church." The voice at the other end was a female one. "What can I do for you, Reverend Mackerel?"

"I want to report a billboard in the Mobile Bay section," I said, glancing out the window over the treetops to an intersection where the offending object was plainly visible. "This is a residential area, where I need not remind you public hoardings are strictly forb—"

"Yes, I know. You're triple-A out there. Please don't get upset, Reverend Mackerel. Go on." The woman—or more likely, girl—was audibly eating something, a fact not calculated to soothe Mackerel's nerves or cool his pique.

"I assume a waiver was granted by the Zoning Board or the signboard wouldn't have got as far as it is," I went on.

"How far is it?"

"It's up! I can see it now from my study window, over there on Cooper Street. And I don't like it."

"What does it say, Reverend Mackerel?"

"It says—" I craned my neck to look out the window, as

From *The Mackerel Plaza*, copyright © 1958 by Peter De Vries. Reprinted by permission of Little, Brown and Company, Boston.

though I had again to verify the testimony of my senses. "It says, 'Jesus Saves.'"

"Oh, yes." There was a silence at the other end, except for an act of deglutition, and then a faint crackling noise which I could believe was that of a successor to a swallowed caramel being unwrapped. "I only work here," the girl declared at last, "but I do remember something about the board deciding that wasn't strictly commercial."

"Commercial! That's not the point. It's vulgar. And the lettering is that awful new phosphorescent stuff—green and orange. No, this is a blight on the landscape and I protest."

"I know what you mean, now that you mention it. You're not the first to complain. The Presbyterians are appalled. The Episcopalians are sick. All the better element there, with property values at stake—"

"Oh, property values! Please get that out of your mind, miss. Do you think I own the parsonage I live in? I'm talking about spiritual values. Spiritual and aesthetic ones. How do you expect me to write a sermon with that thing staring me in the face? How do you expect me to turn out anything fit for civilized consumption?"

"I know. It's terribly *de trop*. And in that part of town—the Mobile Bay section!" There was another silence, but a thoughtful one this time, and unbroken by any of those annoying sounds. Then she said, "But do you think you're entirely right in opposing this? I know this man is a cheap huckster of religion—your religion—but it's the form his faith takes, and don't we need all the faith we can get today? Doesn't the crisis of our time, the mess in which we find ourselves, come from not having any *belief*?"

"Nothing concerns me more than the crisis of our time, Miss—"

"Calico."

"Miss Calico. Nothing concerns me more than the crisis of our time, but, believe me, nothing concerns these people less. They're content precisely to let this thing go hang for the sake of another, which you and I know doesn't exist."

"Well . . ." she said, worriedly.

93

"Oh, come now."

"But the world needs restraint. Some moral order. And that should be on any level the given person can grasp. What does the Apostle Paul say?"

"I have no idea, but Oscar Wilde reminds us that while crime is not vulgar, vulgarity is a crime. Jesus doesn't save any of these people, because all they want to do is boost their paltry souls into heaven, while completely shirking the obligation to *evolve*. What we see around us these days is not a revival at all but a kind of backsliding, and I do mean that—a failure of taste as *well* as nerve." To make my point I had resorted to a phrase from my last Sunday's sermon, and I felt it only fair to the girl to favor her with the entire passage. I therefore continued, "Let us think and do according to our *time*. Let us graft on the Christian principle of self-lessness, as Auden so cogently urges, the Freudian one of maturity, and come up with an ideal suited to our era. Thus two people, each bent on pursuing a different one of these two systems, would die having lived identical lives: one of consideration for others. . . ."

Avalon, Connecticut, lies forty miles out of metropolitan New York on the New Haven commuting track. It is a community where tired successes flee to enact the old charade of seeking roots, knowing they will never have them but must and will, like the fabled mistletoe, live and die without them, suspended between the twin oaks of home and office. They live a kind of hand-to-mouth luxury, never knowing where their next quarterly instalment of taxes or the payment on a third car is coming from. It is a community where the cleaning women have washing compulsions; where lawn benefits are given for folk singers who have escaped from jail; where an Old-fashioned Christmas consists in truly drinking it otherwise than on the rocks for a week. There, Max Kaminsky, Messy Williams and other noted trumpeters, come up from New York to play at Easter services. There, one overhears conversation like, "After each divorce, Monica's disillusioned, and

94

then she goes and gets married again." There, I once heard a woman say, "I've read *Billy Budd* four times and hate it more each time." A special culture, with special and terrible needs, which one tries to meet with all the compassion in one's nature.

Our church is, I believe, the first split-level church in America. It has five rooms and two baths downstairs—dining area, kitchen and three parlors for committee and group meetings—with a crawl space behind the furnace ending in the hillside into which the structure is built. Upstairs is one huge all-purpose interior, divisible into different-sized components by means of sliding walls and convertible into an auditorium for putting on plays, a gymnasium for athletics, and a ballroom for dances. There is a small worship area at one end. This has a platform cantilevered on both sides, with a free-form pulpit designed by Noguchi. It consists of a slab of marble set on four legs of four delicately differing fruitwoods, to symbolize the four Gospels, and their failure to harmonize. Behind it dangles a large multicolored mobile, its interdenominational parts swaying, as one might fancy, in perpetual reminder of the Pauline stricture against those "blown by every wind of doctrine." Its proximity to the pulpit inspires a steady flow of more familiar congregational whim, at which we shall not long demur, going on with our tour to say that in back of this building is a newly erected clinic, with medical and neuro-psychiatric wings, both indefinitely expandable. Thus People's Liberal is a church designed to meet the needs of today, and to serve the whole man. This includes the worship of a God free of outmoded theological definitions and palatable to a mind come of age in the era of Relativity. "It is the final proof of God's omnipotence that he need not exist in order to save us," Mackerel had preached. (I hope I may be indulged these shifts into the third person in relating things about which I am a trifle self-conscious.) At any rate, this aphorism seemed to his hearers so much better than anything Voltaire had said on the subject that he was given an immediate hike in pay and invited out to more dinners than he could possibly eat.

Lawrence Ferlinghetti

Christ Climbed Down

Christ climbed down
from His bare Tree
this year
and ran away to where
there were no rootless Christmas trees
hung with candycanes and breakable stars

Christ climbed down
from His bare Tree
this year
and ran away to where
there were no gilded Christmas trees
and no tinsel Christmas trees
and no tinfoil Christmas trees
and no pink plastic Christmas trees
and no gold Christmas trees
and no black Christmas trees
and no powderblue Christmas trees
hung with electric candles
and encircled by tin electric trains
and clever cornball relatives

Christ climbed down
from His bare Tree
this year

From *A Coney Island of the Mind*, copyright 1955, © 1957 by Lawrence
Ferlinghetti. Reprinted by permission of the publisher, New Directions
Publishing Corporation, New York.

and ran away to where
no intrepid Bible salesmen
covered the territory
in two-tone cadillacs
and where no Sears Roebuck crèches
complete with plastic babe in manger
arrived by parcel post
the babe by special delivery
and where no televised Wise Men
praised the Lord Calvert Whiskey

Christ climbed down
from His bare Tree
this year
and ran away to where
no fat handshaking stranger
in a red flannel suit
and a fake white beard
went around passing himself off
as some sort of North Pole saint
crossing the desert to Bethlehem
Pennsylvania
in a Volkswagen sled
drawn by rollicking Adirondack reindeer
with German names
and bearing sacks of Humble Gifts
from Saks Fifth Avenue
for everybody's imagined Christ child

Christ climbed down
from His bare Tree
this year
and ran away to where
no Bing Crosby carollers
groaned of a tight Christmas
and where no Radio City angels
iceskated wingless
thru a winter wonderland

The Church Camouflaged

into a jinglebell heaven
daily at 8:30
with Midnight Mass matinees
Christ climbed down
from His bare Tree
this year
and softly stole away into
some anonymous Mary's womb again
where in the darkest night
of everybody's anonymous soul
He awaits again
an unimaginable
and impossibly
Immaculate Reconception
the very craziest
of Second Comings

John Betjeman

In Westminster Abbey

Let me take this other glove off
  As the vox humana swells,
And the beauteous fields of Eden
  Bask beneath the Abbey bells.
Here, where England's statesmen lie,
Listen to a lady's cry.

Gracious Lord, oh bomb the Germans.
  Spare their women for Thy Sake,
And if that is not too easy
  We will pardon Thy Mistake.
But, gracious Lord, whate'er shall be,
Don't let anyone bomb me.

Keep our Empire undismembered
  Guide our Forces by Thy Hand,
Gallant blacks from far Jamaica,
  Honduras and Togoland;
Protect them, Lord, in all their fights,
And, even more, protect the whites.

Think of what our Nation stands for,
  Books for Boots' and country lanes,
Free speech, free passes, class distinction,

From *Collected Poems* by John Betjeman, London: John Murray Publishers, Ltd., London, 1959, and Houghton Mifflin Company, Boston, 1959. Reprinted by permission of the publishers.

The Church Camouflaged

Democracy and proper drains.
Lord, put beneath Thy special care
One-eighty-nine Cadogan Square.

Although dear Lord I am a sinner,
    I have done no major crime;
Now I'll come to Evening Service
    Whensoever I have the time.
So, Lord, reserve for me a crown,
And so not let my shares go down.

I will labour for Thy Kingdom,
    Help our lads to win the war,
Send white feathers to the cowards
    Join the Women's Army Corps,
Then wash the Steps around Thy Throne
In the Eternal Safety Zone.

Now I feel a little better,
    What a treat to hear Thy Word,
Where the bones of leading statesmen
    Have so often been interr'd.
And now, dear Lord, I cannot wait
Because I have a luncheon date.

Peter Malton

Instant Baptism

"Please I want the baby done,"
She muttered at the door,
"She's nearly two years old, you know
We've had no time before.
We want her doing Sunday
We've got the cake and all
There'll be thirty-seven coming
And can we have the hall?
We thought perhaps you would have come
And done it long before.
Ask you? But you ought to know
It's what they pay you for.

"You want to talk to Jack and me
About a thing or two?
But Sunday's only three days off
We've far too much to do.
Other children? Yes, we've two.
Of course they've both been done.
To Sunday School? Well no, you see,
They're both too highly strung.
We say they ought to wait and see
(Kids have no need to pray)
If then they want to take up church
We won't stand in their way.

From *Prism Magazine* (London), August 1963. Reprinted by permission of Prism Publications, Limited, London.

The Church Camouflaged

"We promised when they both were done
That as they older grew
That they would learn about the Church
And what they ought to do?
We never! Or at any rate
The parson never said.
Our fault that they know nowt of God?
You must be off your head."

"And so, our man," I told him straight,
I did, I cut up rough,
"We want our Linda doing soon
Without that sort of stuff."
And then, I'm dashed, he smiled and said
With no hard words at all,
"All right, I'll do it Sunday,
And you can have the hall."
Another parson in the house
Who looked a different sort
Had talked about some kid called Grace
And "Contact of a sort."

"If you ask me it's rather daft—
They don't know where they are.
I think this talk of promises
Is taking it too far.
The verger at that other place
Where we had done our Dawn
Just gave a form which we filled in—
The same when Roy was born.
But still, they have their little ways;
They've little else to do
'cept services one day a week
But try some scheme or two."

John Bainbridge

Religion in Texas

If Americans are the world's "churchgoingest" people, as the Reverend Granville T. Walker, pastor of the University Christian Church, in Fort Worth, said in 1960 after returning from a tour of Europe, they must give an extraordinary share of the credit for the achievement to Texans like those in Reverend Mr. Walker's own flock. "On any average Sunday," he has remarked, "I have more people in my congregation than worship in Westminster Abbey or Notre Dame." The same statement could be made by scores of other clergymen throughout the state, and would not be doubted by any visitor who has tried to reach Texans at home between around ten o'clock and one o'clock on Sundays. During those hours, crowds and traffic jams mark the sites of churches, which are, as elsewhere in the United States—only, as might be expected, more so—predominantly Protestant.

In Texas, eighty per cent of the churchgoers belong to one of several Protestant denominations, nineteen per cent are Catholic, and one per cent are Jewish. The Baptists, with thirty-nine per cent of all adult church members, are by far the largest faith in Texas. They are also the richest. The Baptist General Convention of Texas conducts its far-ranging affairs on a yearly budget of some thirteen million dollars, which is approximately three times as much as the state spends

From *The Super-Americans*, copyright © 1961 by John Bainbridge. Reprinted by permission of the author and the publisher, Doubleday & Co., Inc., Garden City, N.Y.

annually to operate its judicial system. Whereas most Texas communities have but one courthouse, the churches seem as plentiful as filling stations. Waco, for example, has some hundred thousand residents and a hundred and twenty-two churches—a ratio between population and places of worship that, Sean O'Faolain was surprised to discover, is even higher than in his native Ireland.

Appropriately, Dallas, the banking capital of the state, is also its religious capital. In addition to being a diocesan seat of the Roman Catholic and Episcopal Churches, Dallas supports the largest Southern Baptist, Methodist, and Southern Presbyterian congregations in the United States. Citizens of Dallas can choose among some eight hundred churches. The biggest—the First Baptist Church, situated in the downtown area—has twelve thousand members, including Billy Graham; employs a staff of fifty; maintains a Sunday school of eighty-seven departments and more than six hundred classes; owns, in addition to its edifice, a seven-story parking and recreational building, containing a university-sized gymnasium, four bowling lanes, and a skating rink; and has an operating budget for the current year of a million one hundred and ninety-five thousand dollars. "This is probably the most stupendous financial program ever undertaken by any church in the history of Christendom," the Reverend Dr. W. A. Criswell, pastor of the church, told his congregation in presenting the 1961 budget. Undismayed, they promptly oversubscribed it, thus recording their customary annual vote of confidence in Dr. Criswell, a firm-jawed, fifty-one-year-old native of Oklahoma who was called to the ministry at the age of six. During his student days, he served as minister in the small Texas community of Pulltight, and for the past seventeen years has been making a name for himself by rapping Roman Catholicism (the election of John F. Kennedy, warned Dr. Criswell during the campaign, would "spell the death of a free church in a free state"), integration ("a thing of idiocy and foolishness"), and evolution ("a hoax perpetrated by the wild imagination of blind, mis-guided scientists"), and in other ways fighting the good fight, as he sees it.

The Highland Park Presbyterian Church of Dallas, though small by Baptist standards, has some five thousand members (making it the largest Southern Presbyterian congregation in the country) and uses a card-indexing system to record vital information about each parishioner, including talents and hobbies. On a typical Sabbath in Dallas, around seventy-five thousand people turn out for Sunday school. They are by no means all youngsters, since in Texas attendance at Sunday school ceases only with death, and classes for grownups are taught by many of the state's leading citizens, including the Governor.

In addition to the abundance of churches, which provides the most obvious evidence of the importance of religion in Super-American life, exhibits of a similar nature, large and small, steadily confront the visitor from the moment he enters the state. Driving in from the west on a summer night, he may pass, on U. S. Highway 62, near El Paso, an illuminated sign of the dimensions used by drive-in movie theatres, which asks, courtesy of the Assembly of God Church, "You Think It's Hot Here?" As he proceeds eastward, he is everywhere struck by the number of church-supported colleges, universities, hospitals, and bookstores, as well as by the amount of new-church construction and old-church expansion, to say nothing of religious installations of a more novel nature. Perhaps the most attractive of these is the Chapel in the Sky, a small oratory, complete with vaulted ceiling, stained-glass windows, eight pews, and non-denominational altar, situated on the thirty-ninth floor of the Southland Center, the newest sky-scraper in Dallas.

In Houston, the visitor, if he still feels in need of spiritual uplift, can pick up the phone any time between nine-thirty and five-thirty and dial Jackson 2-2928, the number of a unique institution called the Telephone Ministry. Unlike the Dial-A-Prayer service in New York, which was originated by the Fifth Avenue Presbyterian Church and provides callers of

Circle 6-4200 with a thirty-second recorded prayer, the Telephone Ministry is completely live. It is sponsored by the Houston Christian Businessmen's Committee and is conducted by Mr. and Mrs. L. E. Showalter, an elderly, religiously inclined couple who spend most of their waking hours on the telephone, listening to problems and giving Christian counsel to callers who have been urged, in newspaper advertisements, to ring up the Ministry "if troubled—burdened—discouraged." If one is not feeling all that bad when he goes to a bowling alley in Houston, he may feel some discouragement when he finds the lanes taken over by several of the seven hundred church teams participating in the Inter-Faith Bowling Tournament, sponsored by the Houston *Post*. "Religion will definitely be an issue," the paper said in announcing the mammoth contest, which the *Post* describes as "a tournament with a mission—to promote fellowship through the mushrooming family sport of bowling."

In Houston, or wherever else in Texas one turns on the radio in the early morning, he is sure to find a rich offering of devotionals, gospel singing, and other religious fare, featuring, for example, the Dallas minister who calls himself Your Radio Friend and Pastor, Reverend J. C. Hibbard; Sister Jack Coe (widow of Brother Jack Coe); and dozens of other members of the clergy who use the ether waves, as they sometimes say, to bring the Gospel to their vast flocks of sinners in Radioland.

If, as the British novelist Walter L. George once remarked, "the newspaper exhibition of the national character is the national character seen under a magnifying glass," the newspapers in Texas might be expected to bring out, perhaps better than anything else, the religious temper of the community. They do, daily and Sunday, in the news and editorial columns and also on the advertising pages. On Saturdays, the newspapers usually contain, in addition to notices placed by individual churches, full-page institutional-type spreads bearing a Biblical message and an exhortation to go to church. ("A Church-Going Family Is a Happier Family"—Tyler *Tele-*

graph.) These are jointly paid for by a number of local business concerns and individuals, whose names are listed but, as the sentiment is phrased in the Waxahachie *Daily Light*, "Who Want as Their Only Return to See a Greater Church Attendance." From time to time, religious matters are discussed in editorials, such as a recent one in the Dallas *News* titled "Pulpit Technique" ("Results come from simplicity, sincerity and inspiration . . . the Bible has few six-bit words"), and obituaries in Texas newspapers give prominence to the religious affiliation of the deceased by stating it near the beginning of the story. The Saturday edition of the Houston *Chronicle* carries an eight-page supplement devoted entirely to religious advertisements and news, including a recent story about a local Episcopal rector whose method of stimulating church attendance was summarized in the bleak headline, "Stay-At-Homes Won't Get Full Burial Rites."

It is the columns of general news, however, that offer the most rewarding coverage of the religious front, concentrating on men of the cloth, both local and national. Among the latter, perhaps none enjoys greater popularity in Texas than Dr. Norman Vincent Peale, whose books and weekly column are syndicated in many Texas newspapers and who is also in wide demand as a speaker before large groups, such as the convention of the Southern Gas Association. On his latest speaking trip to Dallas, eighty-five hundred people turned out to hear "the internationally known author, philosopher, and humanitarian," as Dr. Peale is customarily referred to in the local papers, who stated positively that the world's chief problems today stem from a lack of enough "tough-minded" people to solve them. "A man with fifty problems is twice as alive as a man with twenty-five," he explained. "If you haven't got any problems, you should get down on your knees and ask, 'Lord, don't you trust me any more?' "

Whereas Dr. Peale is ordinarily news in the Texas papers only when visiting there, Billy Graham, another newspaper pet, is seldom out of print, even when out of sight. When he went to Africa last year on a two-month "Safari for Souls," the papers reported his progress in almost daily stories and photographs, including one showing him being kissed by a camel. It is not essential to be a full-fledged minister to capture the fancy of Texas newspapers, but it helps to be at least a lay preacher, like Howard Butt, Jr., a Corpus Christi millionaire in his early thirties whom Graham has designated as worthy of inheriting his mantle. Besides serving as executive vice-president of a supermarket chain doing an annual business of a hundred million dollars, Butt has found time, according to a Houston *Post* story about him titled "Groceries and Gospel Mix Well for Texan," to make more than twenty-five hundred appearances as a preacher, occasionally as a substitute for Graham, in twenty-five states and seven foreign countries.

After professional or part-time preachers, the newspapers favor other interesting people, like Van Cliburn, who also mix the Gospel with their profession. The winning of the International Tchaikowsky Contest made Cliburn a favorite with Texans, but they have subsequently turned him into something of a hero upon learning through the newspapers that he carried a Bible with him to Moscow and, in fact, never travels without it; that before a performance he likes to pray "with the conductor that God give them power to make good music together"; that when at home he never fails to join in daily devotionals with his parents; and that it was they who gave him an admirable philosphy by bringing him up to believe, as he has put it, "Everyone has to work. No one can sit on the tracks and pray. That won't start the train."

Part Four:

A Laugh at the Laity

Humorous hari-kari, or a self-satirizing clergy, doesn't come easily; so most satire of religion is by laity. But vanity's looking glass is mirrored on both sides, and those who sit in the pews cannot escape the reflection.

OSBERT SITWELL, of that remarkable English Roman Catholic family, was a writer of such elegant taste that, in a world of so much philistinism, he turned naturally to the avocation of what he called "nit-wit baiting." As he portrays the stuffed piety of the laity, even surrounding nature is inhibited by such a blight. CLARENCE DAY spent most of his days as an invalid who, nonetheless, turned out a series of charming novels of family life. His satire is grounded in genuine affection for its objects. The dominant note is that of ironic tenderness. Year after year, in his classes at Yale Divinity School, as in his writing, HALFORD LUCCOCK exemplified two things quite important in the history of satire: one, that it can be done very well by those most devoted to the church and, two, that when satire is combined with a genuinely winsome and affectionate spirit it can be doubly effective. Too often, as with Swift or the later Mark Twain, an inner vitriol can spoil even the best of writing. Luccock probably removed more stuffing per square seminarian than any other teacher of his day. ELIZABETH BERRYHILL, like Professor Luccock, works with seminary students. Anyone about to launch future ministers from academic

109

shipyards develops a natural nervousness lest a redeeming sense of humor not be built in. The skit printed here is pure satirical joshing. It is a lampoon of church busy-work, organized with military briskness. Comic relief comes to the rescue of ecclesiastical silliness.

This section contains two beguiling examples of Jewish religious satire. The richness of Jewish humor is lost on many non-Jews who, not having lived in a Jewish community and not knowing the nuances of either Yiddish or Hebrew, fail to catch all the innuendoes. S. T. HECHT's story is one of a half-dozen or so he wrote for *Commentary* magazine. Each of the tales is centered around the mythical town of Reedsville, somewhere between Hackensack and Hoboken, N.J. Mr. Hecht revels in the affectionate satire which underscores the problems of a Jewish minority. The pressures and the pain and the joy of being a Jew has *forced* the development of one of the world's best senses of humor and satire: that peculiarly Jewish combination of poignancy and wit. HARRY GOLDEN, Editor of *The Carolina Israelite*, has been called the Jewish Will Rogers. It's a compliment to Will. Golden grew up on the lower East Side of New York City, and in his portraits of Jewish life the satire ranges from the tenderest to the sharpest. WERNER PELZ is a minister in the Church of England, a well-known writer, and a Christian existentialist. His account of his useless sermon about the agony of the world, falling like rain on the umbrellaed consciences of the laity, is an altogether true testimony to what happens over and over, to what has broken the heart of more than one preacher. *The National Catholic Reporter* is a weekly magazine tuned to the new generation of Catholics: ecumenically minded, with no ghetto defense mechanisms, throwing praise and blame about with fine impartiality among priests, prelates, and people. BERNARD BASSET is an English Jesuit in great demand as both lecturer and retreat leader. He has a fine nose for the popular superstitions of the pious. Not for him those nunneries where the height of landscape gardening is reached when a fence-rosary made of bowling balls and rose bushes advertises the faith.

Osbert Sitwell

Church Parade

The flattened sea is harsh and blue—
Lies stiff beneath—one tone, one hue,
White concertina waves unfold
The painted shimmering sands of gold.

Each bird that whirls and wheels on high
Must strangle, stifle in, its cry,

For nothing that's of Nature born
Should seem so on the Sabbath morn.

The terrace glitters hard and white,
Bedaubed and flecked with points of light

That flicker at the passers-by—
Reproachful as a curate's eye,

And china flowers, in steel-bound beds,
Flare out in blues and flaming reds;

Each blossom, rich and opulent,
Stands like a soldier; and its scent

Is turned to Camphor in the air.
No breath of wind would ever dare

From *Selected Poems—Old and New* by Osbert Sitwell, London: Gerald Duckworth & Co. Ltd., 1943. Reprinted by permission of the
publisher.

A Laugh at the Laity

To make the trees' plump branches sway,
Whose thick green leaves hang down to pray.

The stiff, tall churches vomit out
Their rustling masses of devout;

Tall churches whose stained Gothic night
Refuses to receive the light.

Watch how the stately walk along
Toward the terrace, join the throng

That paces carefully up and down
Above a cut-out cardboard town!

With prayer-book rigid in each hand,
They look below at sea and sand:

The round contentment in their eyes
Betrays their favourite fond surmise,

That all successful at a trade
Shall tread an eternal Church-Parade,

And every soul that's sleek and fat
Shall gain a heavenly top-hat.

From out the Church's Gothic night,
Past beds of blossoms china-bright,
Beneath the green trees' porous shade,
We watch the sea-side Church-Parade.

Clarence Day

My Father and His Pastors

A man who accepts a religion without being religious lets himself in for more hardships than one would suppose. My father persisted most manfully in going to church; and he usually started around there at peace with the world, and settled himself down contentedly in his end seat; but somehow before very long his expression would darken, as his hopes of hearing a sensible service little by little were dashed; and he came out in an inflamed state of mind that could not have been good for him.

The Episcopal service in general he didn't criticize—it was stately and quiet; but the sermon, being different every Sunday, was a very bad gamble. And once in a while there would be an impromptu prayer that he would take great offense at. Sometimes he disliked its subject or sentiments—if he chanced to be listening. Sometimes he decided it was too long or its tone too lugubrious. I remember seeing him so restive during a prayer of that kind, that—although the entire congregation was kneeling in reverence—he suddenly gave a loud snort, sat up straight in his pew, and glared at the minister's back as though planning to kick it.

Toward the latter part of his life Father found a minister whose sermons he liked. This was the Reverend Mr. Henshaw of Rye, where he lived in the summer. Mr. Henshaw wasn't

From *God and My Father*, copyright 1931, 1932 by Clarence Day. Reprinted by permission of the publisher, Alfred A. Knopf, Inc., New York.

"one of these pious fellows," Father said, with approval—though why piety was so unsuited to the clergy was never explained. And some years before this, one summer on the Hudson near Tarrytown, there was a Mr. Wenke, an earnest young cleric, who also found favor. But this was mostly because one of the vestry, old Mr. John Rutland, was very strict with Mr. Wenke about the length of his sermons. Mr. Rutland had got it into his head that all sermons should end at twelve, sharp; and if he saw Mr. Wenke being carried away by his own eloquence, he would take out his watch and stare ominously, first at him, then at it. Pretty soon Mr. Wenke's roving eye would be caught and held by this sight. He would falter or sometimes almost choke in the midst of his flow, then lamely end his remarks, and get out of the pulpit.

In the city at this same later period Father went to St. Bartholomew's, and there too the various clergymen suited him, though not quite so well. He liked St. Bartholomew's. The church itself was comfortable, and the congregation were all the right sort. There was Mr. Edward J. Stuyvesant, who was president of three different coal mines, and Admiral Prentice, who had commanded the Fleet, and old Mr. Johns of the *Times;* and bank directors and doctors and judges—solid men of affairs. The place was like a good club. And the sermon was like a strong editorial in a conservative newspaper. It did not nag at Father, it attacked the opposition instead; it gave all wrongheaded persons a sound trouncing, just the way Father would have.

But nothing is perfect. After Father had made himself at home in this reliable temple he discovered too late that even here a man wasn't safe. The rector began talking about the need for what he called a New Edifice. He said the church had a leak in the roof, and the neighborhood was changing to business, and that they had received a good offer for the property and had better move elsewhere. This gave Father an unsettled feeling. He wished to stay put. But the rector kept stirring things up until he at last got his way.

Committees were appointed, and active teams of workers

were organized, who began to collect large subscriptions from every parishioner. Father paid no attention to all this. It was no plan of his. If they insisted on having better quarters, he would try to enjoy them, but except from this effort the rest of it was not his affair. It was only when he was made to see that he, too, would have to subscribe, that Father became roused and startled. This had never occurred to him. He said he might have known it was just a damn scheme to get money.

I don't recall how much he gave in the end, but I think it was a thousand dollars. The reason Mother thought that he would probably have to give more, was that our pew was way up in front; it was—so to speak—in a fine section. All our neighbors were prominent. There may have been plenty of ordinary Christians in other parts of the building, but I did not see them. Furthermore this pew, though a small one, had cost Father five thousand dollars, and parishioners were being asked to give as much as the cost of their pews. Father had hated to invest all that money in a mere place to sit, but he could sell out again some day, and meanwhile he had a good pew. He rented the one in Rye for a hundred and twenty dollars a year; but a family that wanted a good pew at St. Bartholomew's in those old days used to buy it. They went to the sexton or somebody, and told him what size and so forth, and after a while he would negotiate a purchase for them from some other parishioner. Pews were like seats on the stock exchange. Nobody speculated in pews, of course, and they rarely changed hands; but they went up and down in price, naturally, as the demand rose or fell; and after Father had bought his— most unwillingly—from old Mr. Baggs, he used to ask Mother periodically for the current quotation. Mother disliked to get this. It obliged her to ask the sexton, who was dignified, and who didn't like to quote pews; and another objection was that after Father bought they went down in value. When she came home with the news that the last sale had been for thirty-two hundred, Father said she had led him into this against his own better judgment, and now the bottom was dropping out of the market, and he never would get his money back. "Old Baggs, *he* knew. He was a shrewd one," he declared. "Egad, yes! He knew when to sell." And he swore that if that damn pew ever went up again he would unload it on somebody. . . .

The clergyman there [at the Church of the Peace Everlasting] was the Reverend Dr. Owen Lloyd Garden. He was a plump, bustling man, very goodhearted and pleasant; though in spite of his goodheartedness and kindness I never felt at ease with him. He never seemed to speak to me personally, but to a thing called My Child. He was more at home speaking to a large audience than to a small boy, however. He had warm and sympathetic feelings toward people *en masse*. The congregation responded to this quality in him and liked him; and he not only kept the pews filled but he sometimes attracted such crowds that Mr. Dryden would scurry by, with his whiskers flying straight out behind him, putting chairs in the aisle.

Doctor Garden had come over to New York from England, but by descent he was Welsh. He had a broad red face, thick black hair, and a square blue-black beard. His robes were red, black, and white. His strong English accent was a point in his favor in an Episcopal church; it seemed to go well with the service. But owing, we understood, to his Welsh descent, he was very emotional, and he used to plead with us at times in his sermons in a sort of high mellow howl. My father disliked this. In the first place he heartily detested having anyone plead with him; in the second place Doctor Garden seldom could plead without crying. It wasn't put on at all; he was deeply moved by his own words. The atmosphere became tense and still when he leaned from his pulpit and stretched out his arms yearningly to us and sobbed, "Oh, my people." The whole church was hushed. At such moments Father would testily stir in his seat. "The damned Welshman, there he goes sniveling again," he would mutter.

Another thing he detested was the picture Doctor Garden drew, sometimes, of a businessman sitting in his offiice at the close of his day. Doctor Garden didn't cry over this, to be sure, but he grew gentle and solemn—he spoke as though he himself were standing at that businessman's side, like an unseen Presence, a loving Good Influence, evoking the man's better self. He apparently had only the haziest ideas of a business office, but he drew on his imagination freely to fill in the picture. He would describe how this hardheaded man sat there, surrounded by ledgers, and how after studying them closely and harshly for hours he would chance to look out of his window at the light in God's sky, and then it would come to him that money and ledgers were dross. Whereat, as the gathering twilight spread over the city, this strange waxwork figure of a businessman would bow his head, and with streaming eyes resolve to devote his life to Far Higher Things.

"Oh, damn," Father would burst out, so explosively that the man across the aisle jumped, and I would hear old Mrs. Tillotson, in the second pew behind, titter.

Aside from the wild untruth of such pictures of business, from Father's point of view the whole attitude involved was pernicious. Anyone dreamy enough to think of money as "dross" was bound to get himself in hot water; that went without saying; it was a sign both of ignorance of, and of disrespect for, finance. Father had more respect for finance than he had for the church. When he left the financial district behind him to visit the church, he felt as I suppose Moses felt coming down from the mountain. Moses found people blind to his mountain and worshiping a calf idiotically, and Father found Doctor Garden capering around something he called Higher Things. Well, let him caper if he wanted to—that was all he was good for. My father was a more charitable Moses who expected no better. But this flighty parson went farther— he wanted Moses to join him! Betray finance for this stuff and nonsense! It was enough to make a man sick.

Halford Luccock

Like a Mighty Army

I met the pastor of St. John's-by-the-Gas-Station last Monday. He was all lit up—not alcoholically but emotionally. I said, "You must have been pretty good yesterday."

"Better than that," he replied, "I had a guest artist take over. And he took everybody over."

"How come?" I asked.

"It was Layman's Sunday. Usually that Sunday brings joy, like a visit to the dentist. A good thing, but better to look back on than forward to. This year I slipped one over on them. You know Jimmy Mitchell, just back from two years in the army in Korea? I figured he would give Layman's Sunday a shot in the arm, but I didn't reckon on him blowing the place up. He refused at first. Then, with a funny light in his eye, he said he would speak if I had the congregation sing 'Onward Christian Soldiers' just before he began . . . So I had them give forth with song, and then Jimmy let loose. He didn't waste any time in shadow-boxing. He waded right in. This is what he said: 'You have been singing

> Like a mighty army
> Moves the church of God.

That might have been all right once. The trouble is now that just about ten million men know exactly how an army moves. And it doesn't move the way a lot of you folks at St. John's

From *The Christian Century*, February 6, 1952, copyright 1952 by The Christian Century Foundation. Reprinted by permission of the publisher.

do—or do not. Suppose the army accepted the lame excuses that many of you people think are good enough to serve as an alibi for not attending Church Parade.

" 'Imagine this, if you can. Reveille seven a.m., squads on the parade ground. The sergeant barks out, "Count fours." "One!" "Two!" "Three!" Number Four missing. "Where's Private Smith?"

" ' "Oh," pipes up a chap by the vacant place, "Mr. Smith was too sleepy to get up this morning. He was out late last night and needed the sleep. He said to tell you that he would be with you in spirit."

" ' "That's fine," says the sergeant. "Remember me to him."

" ' "Where's Brown?" asks the sergeant.

" ' "Oh," puts in another chap, "he's out playing golf. He gets only one day a week for recreation, and you know how important that is."

" ' "Sure, sure," is the sergeant's cheerful answer. "Hope he has a good game. Where's Robinson?"

" ' "Robinson," explains a buddy, "is sorry not to greet you in person. But he is entertaining guests today and of course couldn't come. Besides, he was at drill last week."

" ' "Thank you," says the sergeant, smiling. "Tell him he is welcome any time he is able to drop in."

" 'Honest, now, did any conversation like that ever happen in any army? Don't make me laugh. If any G.I. tried to pull that stuff he would get twenty days in the guardhouse. Yet you hear stuff like that every week in the church, and said with a straight face, too.

" 'Like a mighty army! Why, if St. John's really moved like a mighty army, a lot of you folks would be court-martialed!'

"That was the general drift," said the pastor gleefully.

"Too bad the stay-aways didn't hear it," I remarked.

"Don't worry. I have it on a tape recorder, and I am going to spring it on them next Easter, instead of the Second Lesson."

Forward March!

Elizabeth Berryhill

Many Are Called, but Few Are Chosen

[*The stage contains only a small table on which are a pitcher and a glass. Inspirational, uplifting music is heard. The narrator walks briskly onto the stage. He is a very sincere fellow, hearty and friendly. He mouths the words, synchronizing his lip movement with the sound of his recorded voice.*]

NARRATOR 1

Good evening, fellow Americans and fellow members of the United Presbyterian Church, U.S.A!

[*A surge of music, during which he drinks from the glass of water on the table*]

Well, it's Fall again, folks—and you know what *that* means! Fall means "Stewardship," friends—and "Stewardship" means the Every-Member Canvass—and the Every-Member Canvass means—Well, just what *does* it mean? Do *you* know?

[*Music up and out. He carries off his table with the pitcher and glass and returns to the stage*]

We've thought a lot about the answer to that question, folks, and we hope that tonight you're going to think a lot about it too. And because we want to help you to do just that, we've decided to take a hard look together at the way *one* church tackled its particular Stewardship program and conducted its Every-Member Canvass. So let's go now to Eastminster Presbyterian Church to see what we can see—and learn what we can learn.

[*Music: "Church in the Wildwood." Narrator 1 exits*]

NARRATOR 2 [*Voice only. A very objective reporter-observer type*]

Eastminster Presbyterian Church is an average church on an average street in an American city of average size. Eastminster has a pastor, a minister of Christian Education, a secretary, the usual number of fellowship groups, one Girl Scout and seven Boy Scout troops, a Sunday School that needs more teachers, a choir that needs more tenors, and . . .

[*Here various members of the congregation enter in pairs and walk across the stage, chatting, laughing, arguing, being in general very human and not looking "religious" at all!*]

. . . a congregation of average size which is made up of just about the kind of average people you'd expect to see in this kind of an average church.

[*The members of the congregation have at this point cleared the stage*]

But in spite of its apparent social and cultural unity, theologically speaking, Eastminster cannot be easily pushed into any convenient pigeonhole, though there is considerable agreement among the congregation as to the nature of God and His actions.

WOMAN [*tremulously*]

God is love!

MAN [*decidedly*]

God helps those who help themselves!

121

A Laugh at the Laity

TWO CHILDREN [*singing*]

Jesus loves me, this I know,
For the Bible tells me so—

NARRATOR

And also considerable agreement as to the nature of man:

WOMAN [*tremulously*]

We're all miserable sinners!

MAN [*forcefully*]

We're totally depraved!

TWO MORE CHILDREN [*singing*]

Jesus loves me, this I know,
For the Bible tells me so—

NARRATOR

There are also dissenting views of what might be termed a
less orthodox and perhaps more liberal nature:

WOMAN

We must think positively!

MAN [*this is the word!*]

God helps those who help themselves!

TWO MORE CHILDREN [*singing*]

Jesus loves me, this I know,
For the Bible tells me so—

NARRATOR

But despite the fact of the wide disparity in what, it might
be admitted, is often an unconscious theology, the members of
Eastminster enjoy a very real fellowship, as a typical week's
schedule of an average month indicates:

E. Berryhill: *Many Are Called, Few Are Chosen*

MAN

Monday night: Men's Club dinner.

WOMAN

Tuesday noon: Women's Club luncheon.

MAN

Wednesday night: Basketball practice—followed by punch and cookies.

MAN

Thursday night: Choir dinner—followed by practice.

WOMAN

Friday night: Baked bean supper—community sing.

YOUNG GIRL

Saturday afternoon: Family picnic—games for all ages.

MAN

Sunday morning: Worship at 9:00 and 11:00 . . .

WOMAN

Coffee hour after each service!

NARRATOR

But food and fun and fellowship, important as they are to Eastminster, have not obscured for the congregation the vision of the church's mission:

1ST MAN

There's more to it—than just—us!

2ND MAN

It's bigger—higher—somehow!

123

1ST WOMAN

Peace!—of mind?

3RD MAN

Judgment!

NARRATOR

And out of this vision has come the *real* thrust of its stewardship program.

1ST MAN

We've got to be dynamic!

1ST WOMAN

Organize!

3RD WOMAN

Coordinate!

2ND MAN

Mobilize our forces!

3RD MAN

Get out of the pews and get to work!

NARRATOR

The result? The Eastminster Every-Member Canvass, the heart of Eastminster's Stewardship Program, and thus of our study tonight.

[*Music: a stirring march*]

NARRATOR

The Stewardship Department of Eastminster recognized from the beginning that its first and most important task lay in the recruitment of canvassers with a clear understanding of personal responsibility and *obligation*. With this understanding recruitment began:

[*A man comes onto the stage, sits by a table and picks up the telephone*]

RECRUITER [*dials a number—very business-like*]

Hello, George? This is Ralph Taylor. Yeah. Yeah—I'm fine. Fine. Say, George, remember that contract for plumbing fixtures I threw your way on the Kaiser job a few months back? No. No. I told you at the time I didn't want anything out of it. No, George, I meant it. But, as a matter of fact, George, I do have a little matter on my mind I wanted to talk to you about. Well, it's nothing much. Just this year's Every-Member Canvass at the church. I was wondering if you could take the time to—

[*He goes on talking in pantomime as the narrator resumes. During the following speech, a big, military-type map is placed on the playing area, covered up*]

NARRATOR

After recruitment was complete and the canvassers committed, the planning work began. Eastminster was fortunate in that it had in its congregation an organizational expert: a retired Army Colonel who was used to getting things done right. The Colonel wasted no time in going to the heart of the matter, calling his troops together in the church late one sunny October Sunday almost immediately following the coffee hour following the second service.

[*Scene: The basement of Eastminster Presbyterian Church. A large map (though covered at the beginning) is centrally located in the speaker's dais. When uncovered, it will be revealed as a map of a city, marked with arrows, circles, etc., in red and black. The Colonel enters, with a long pointer in his hand. He acts as if someone had called out "ten-hut!" He turns to the audience*]

125

COLONEL

At ease, all right, gentlemen. And ladies. Let's have your full attention, please. Now first, let's check our roster. Able Group?

VOICE FROM AUDIENCE

Here!
[*The Colonel glares*]
Oh, I beg your pardon! All present and accounted for, sir!

COLONEL

Baker Group?

ANOTHER VOICE

All present and accounted for, sir!

COLONEL

Charlie Group?

ANOTHER VOICE

All present and accounted for, sir!

COLONEL

Dog Group?

ANOTHER VOICE [*Woman*]

Now let's see. Oh, yes—one sick, one visiting relatives out of town, one absent without leave, otherwise present, sir!

COLONEL

Roger. Now men—and women—I don't have to tell you why we're here. As a great soldier once said: Ours not to reason why, ours but to do or die. So let's get down to the business at hand. Any questions at this point? [*No one speaks*] All right.

E. Berryhill: *Many Are Called, Few Are Chosen*

[*Looks at his watch and makes minor adjustments*]

It is now—exactly—twelve-hundred fifty hours. Synchronize your watches please! We will move out at exactly thirteen-hundred and rendezvous back here at exactly seventeen-hundred. That means we've got four hours to move into our sectors, drop our leaflets, hit the enemy, secure our objectives and move out again fast! It's a big job—it's a hard job—but let me emphasize, gentlemen—ladies—it can be done if we have the guts to do it! Any questions at this point? [*No one speaks*] All right.

[*He moves to the map, pulls off the cover*]

Now this is a map of our overall large objective. Each group's attack objective is clearly marked, as you can see. Able Group—Sector 1; Baker Group—Sector 2; Charlie Group—Sector 3; and Dog Group—Sector 4. These sectors are all arranged geographically and in most instances, according to the plan of streets and the direction in which people in the area are accustomed to travel. This means that if you move according to plan, no one—repeat, no one—should be able to get past one or another of your platoon sectors. But the plan is everything!

All right, gentlemen—ladies. [*Checks watch*] You have five minutes in which to prepare yourselves, pick up your leaflets, check your individual sector maps and name cards. Remember, move carefully but move fast!

And now, good luck—and God bless you.

[*Music: Final bars, "Onward, Christian Soldiers"*]

127

S. T. Hecht

Oh Grave, Thy Victory

When Jake Hammer died he sure made us trouble. Naturally, you'll ask how could Jake make trouble if he was dead?
That's precisely the point.

Among our Jewish people, it appears, you shouldn't die in
the summer, not if you don't want to make trouble. I was
talking to Morris Teitelbaum from Newark, where they have
shuls [synagogues] by the dozen and some even with two
rabbis; but over there too, it seems, they've got the same kind
of *tsores* [troubles]. Of course when a poor man dies in the
summer, the assistant rabbi takes over. But if one of the
bigwigs, a Barney Rossman, heaven forbid, passes on and the
senior rabbi, naturally, is away on vacation, God knows where
—then you'll hear about it, I promise you. And so will the
rabbi—on his return.

"How am I to know?" he will try to defend himself.

"For fifteen thousand a year," the cheeky one on the Board
will tell him, "you are supposed to know!"

Compute the risks then of dying during the summer in a
little burg with only one rabbi, then multiply by two for a
shtetl [small town] like Reedville, N.J., where the best we can
afford is a part-time rabbi. Plainly, in the summer is altogether
a bad time for Jews to be dying. But there is something even
worse, hazard unimaginable, so to speak, and that is to pass

From an article by Samuel Theodore Hecht published in *Commentary*
(New York), September, 1953. Reprinted and abridged by permission
of the author.

away during a summer weekend. In Reedville it's like dropping dead in a desert.

Just exactly when is a good time for Jews or anyone else to die, you can't ever be really sure. It's one of those things you put off as long as possible, like paying your shul dues and pledges. As for which day of the week is best, some say Friday night; some say Saturday. Those in the know maintain that during Yom Kippur is the *ne plus ultra* of all occasions, especially after Kol Nidre. Not only is this the high dramatic moment in the whole Jewish religious calendar—it'll prove, besides, that at heart you were truly a saint, the slander and backbiting of your fellow committee members to the contrary notwithstanding.

Jake died in a hot July, and almost instantly our community was set by the ears trying to decide if he was fit to be given a Jewish burial.

When he heard the news, Mr. Benny Itzkowitz—if you don't remember him I can tell you that Mrs. Greenspan once confidentially told me he was a "pillow from the synagogue" —Itzkowitz at once declared outright: "Hammer ain't no Jew!"

Now unless one adheres to the dictum that "Once an Englishman always an Englishman," Jake Hammer really had a hard time qualifying as a Jew. Naturally, those who had eased up on their own observances championed Jake's cause. But the Orthodox wanted none of him! And that's where, as I said, Jake Hammer made us the trouble.

It was summer and our part-time rabbi, poor fellow, always had to take a job in one Jewish camp or another where, believe me, some kids get all the Jewishness they'll ever have. Reedville in the summer, to all intents and purposes, returns to its early Christian purity, what with the Jews at the beaches or the mountains.

Mrs. Hammer, I've been told, first called up the Presbyterian minister, but he quickly disabused her of her notions, not rudely if you please, but tactfully you understand, so she was able to put two and two together and realize for the first

time in her namby-pamby neither-Jewish nor-Christian existence, that not being baptized, her Jake wasn't exactly kosher
merchandise for a church burial. "It would be much more
appropriate, Mrs. Hammer, if Mr. Hammer were interred as a
Jew." My mother would have said, *"Noch'n toyt iz er goveren
a Yid."* [After his demise Jake became a Jew.]

First indications were that nobody would take Jake—truly,
A Man Without a Cemetery. We, officially Orthodox, not
only lacked a rabbi to do the honors. There were those among
us—plenty—who didn't feel that Jake would exactly constitute
an ornament to our *Bes Oylem* [cemetery]. His monument, to
be sure, would be big enough. It would jut out in our modest
cemetery, rise and declare itself like the Obelisk in Central
Park. But during his life, I have been given to understand, he
in no way identified himself with our people. I've also been
told that he was ashamed of our Reedville Jews.

"Tell me!" Itzkowitz clamored. "Tell me from at least two
mitzvahs [deserving deeds] what he done, and I'll say is all
right he shall lay in our cemetery."

Behold zealotry forgetful of the goodness of God! Our
father Abraham, pleading for the city of Sodom, might have
saved it had he been able to produce *one* good man. Itzkowitz
wanted *two* mitzvahs. Never had Hammer given a cent to
Jewish charities, not until our veterans in the UJA Year of
Destiny campaign flushed him from the thicket and somehow
extracted twenty-five bucks from his hide. As "Colonel" Abe
Klein remarked at the time: *"A hor fun a chazer is oych gut."*
[Even a bristle from a pig is something gained.]

Jake Hammer lived alone with his wife in a very nice white
house in a very exclusive part of Reedville. His lawn was long
and wide, and the house itself sat well back behind a wall of
tall rhododendron. What he did with his wife alone there,
none of us could figure out. A sort of mysterious character,
whom the old-timers among our Jews in Reedville had long
ago given up. He was reputed to have had some sort of
business in New York, just what, nobody knows. By the time I
arrived on the Reedville scene he was already retired, white-

haired, quite dignified, walking once as I saw him when he was pointed out to me, with his large head, stooped shoulders, all alone on the lawn toward evening before the mosquitoes begin their nightly blood collection for their own boys in the service. Charlie Parker, one of my *goyishe* [gentile] buddies, pointing him out said, "Waxy, there goes one of your lost brethren," and he gave me a fill-in on Jake Hammer. "You should try to bring him back to the tabernacle. Do him good!"

In his cellar Jake had a valuable collection of shaving mugs and tonsorial bottles which he kept in a showcase built for the purpose, with doors that locked to make it easy shipping to exhibitions. He also prided himself on his library of Americana over which he made a great to-do but never read. His ambition, as I have learned from sources other than Greenspan, was to make himself acceptable to the goyim. He gave to the Boy Scouts of America, to Father Flanagan's Boys' Town, to the Red Cross, and during his brief marriage to the Presbyterian Church he made more than tolerable contributions to the church itself, to their missions, and toward a fund for a new parish house they were hoping to erect. He must have once thought to buy his way in.

After Jake Hammer's death our Reedville library held quite an exhibition of his books. The Reedville *Republican Sentinel* reported the event in proper spirit, but never a word about his former flirtations with Presbyterianism. So he lived, quietly, mysteriously, a lonesome figure of a man who, as he aged, perhaps had felt he had made some blunders and that the best way out was to keep behind his trees and bushes. His one son, Michael, married a *shiksa* [gentile girl], of course, changed his name to Hammond, and through his wife succeeded where his father failed and was safely brought to Jesus.

Mrs. Hammer was, I guess, the villain in the piece. She was devilishly eager to become a member of the Reedville Women's Club, and as it's said about a camel and the eye of a needle, that's how much chance there ever has been for a Jewess to elbow herself into that outfit. My own home isn't far from their club and I'll have to allow it's a darned nice-looking piece of real estate, but the dames I see rolling up to its doors, for my money you can put 'em in one barrel and make pickled snobs from the whole lot of 'em. Mrs. Adelaide Waller, who belongs to that choice group and whom my wife and I got to know by buying through Reedville's Co-op, swears that the women are the stupidest lot of stuffed brassieres you ever saw in a mirror or elsewhere.

Mrs. Hammer, according to her, was under the delusion that gentile social doors would fly open once she and Jake joined the fanciest church in town. "You know the pay-off," Mrs. Waller said to us a year after Jake died. "The Women's Club wanted to make some money. They read in the *Sentinel* about Jake's having those shaving mugs and pretty bottles, so they wrote to Mrs. Hammer asking would she please lend them to be exhibited at the club for a charitable purpose. *And the damn fool did it!*" It must have been quite a come-down for her to discover that joining the church didn't automatically bestow membership in the Women's Club. Poor Mrs. Hammer!

That July day Jake died—he said he was tired, went to lie down on a sofa, and poof! *oys* [no more] Jake. He was gone! Mrs. Hammer called Reverend Sutton whose hand she had shaken on Sundays as he stood in the shadowed and venerable entrance to our Presbyterian Church, and he, as I've said, had to let her down gently. Miserable critter! She thought she was through with us. Go tell her that hard as it is to be a Jew, it is even harder to quit being one. When you're alive, brother, you can ramble as you darn please, but after you're a goner, my boy, that's when you come home again—like it or not.

"What am I to do?" she quavered. The doctor, of course, wrote the necessary certification, but that's only the beginning. If you've been lucky enough thus far never to have to go through the agony of "arranging things," let me advise you right off—join whatever is necessary, even our little Ahavath Israel, superior as you may feel to it. It pays.

Speaks now Mr. Greenspan in his own particular way: "Rings the telephone one morning when is very hot the weather, and says a voice from which I never before heard and is asking, 'Is this Mr. Greenspan?' I say yes, and is a voman's voice which I still don't recognize and is saying, 'Mr. Greenspan, this is Mrs. Hammer.' 'What can I do, mam?' I say, and she says, 'Is dead Mr. Hammer.' In a minute I remember, and I say how sorry I am from the sad news. Sad I wasn't, but glad I wasn't neither. After all, is a human being, why should I be glad he dies? True, he didn't do us no good, but harm he didn't do us neither. 'I'm needing help,' she says, and is crying the voman. Is a funny thing mit people, Mr. Waxman. For years they lives in a community and never pays a cent to a shul or church, but comes time when they needing it, they expecting shall be there. Is coming to them! Right now is in town lots of young Jews mit children which don't pay nothing to the shul. Comes Yom Kippur they expecting seats which ain't members and they don't belonging to nothing. When grows up the boy needs to be Bar Mitzvah—step right in! But if we ain't having everything nice and ready for them, they is going mad, turning up the nose and saying 'Such a dump!' We needing to keep up a cemetery for them, mit a shul, mit a rabbi, mit a cantor for the Holidays—*un alles oyf trombe* [all for peanuts]!"

Our Reedville Ahavath Israel cemetery committee consisted of one man, whom Greenspan called up at once.

"Is Jake Hammer dead," he said to Leo Lifshitz.

"So what?" says Leo. "Is none of our business."

"Mrs. Hammer wants we shall bury him."

"Let her ask the priest from the Presbyterian Church."

"Listen, Leo. Is not I'm saying you wrong. But the voman is needing help. She wants a Jewish burial."

"*Nu!*" cried Leo. "*Di malachim tanzen in himel* [the angels rejoice on high]. For twenty years he never give a penny to nothing and now we should bury him. The *chutzpah* [nerve] of the rich! He didn't even buy no plot from us!"

Greenspan called Mrs. Hammer, explained that our rabbi was away on vacation—only a slight exaggeration—and incidentally informed her that we had no record of their ever having purchased a grave from us.

133

Her son, Michael, who had arrived by then, took over the telephone at this point and he asked Greenspan if there would be any objections to having his father removed to Finnegan's Funeral Home.

"You do mit him as you like," said Greenspan.

"Will a rabbi go there?"

Greenspan gave him the bitter truth. From a goyish funeral parlor no rabbi which has self-respect would walk in.

"Mine advice is you shall leave him where he is."

"Will you get us a rabbi to take care of everything?"

Greenspan, good soul, said he would try.

"But a plot on the cemetery you must first buy from us!"

News travels fast in Reedville. Within the hour our Jewish merchants on Main Street were either pro-Hammer or anti-Hammer. But there was one detail on which they all saw eye to eye: the price of the plot was to cover some twenty years' dues in the synagogue, plus a rabbi's fee of a hundred, plus incidentals such as the cost of a coffin, a gratuity to the Chevre Kedishe—the Holy Brotherhood, usually consisting of some poor old Jews—for who else wants to wash a dead body, pare the nails, and otherwise set up the deceased for a proper audience with the King of Kings? For a nice round sum of a thousand dollars, it was agreed we would bury Jake Hammer and take care of all the arrangements.

Harry Golden

I Never Miss an Auf Probe

"Auf probe," literally, "on probation," refers specifically to the trial sermon and congregational interview of a new candidate for the pulpit. "Let's go and look over the new rabbi."

If I hear of an auf probe anywhere within a radius of fifty miles, I am off like a fireman. There is no event in our culture which is so rich in human interest.

In the old days the rabbi had a cinch. If he could keep in the good graces of the president of the congregation, he was in like Flynn. For all I know this may still be true in some of the congregations of the metropolitan centers. But down South it is an entirely different matter. In fact there was never a time when *one man* made the decisions in the congregations of Dixie, and the reason was economics rather than democracy. In the large cities you have many strata of society within a single organization. There are manufacturers, bankers, white-collar workers, workmen, and the few men at the top quite naturally step into their proper positions of leadership. But in the South we represent, in the main, a single proprietary class. What we really have here are congregations composed almost exclusively of Medicine Men and no Indians—with practically every member qualified to sit on the dais.

Just imagine what that means for a rabbi.

The interesting fact about all of this is that it parallels that religio-social life of the Gentile community, particularly the Baptists and Methodists, who enjoy autonomy in their individual churches. In fact, one of the outstanding Baptist clergymen told me that the best way to retain a pulpit is to make a simple statement at the first interview. "Gentlemen of the board, I am the 'transient' here and you are the permanents; tell me how you want it done, and I will do it."

Another parallel is concerned with the actual mechanics of asking a clergyman to resign his pulpit, when the "leaders" feel that he has not met their requirements. The leaders know they must act quickly—within a year or, at most, two years. Once the rabbi or Protestant minister occupies the pulpit for three or four years, the leaders have lost their initiative. They can only keep praying that the man gets a call from another congregation. The reason for this is that the majority of the congregation is not at all close to the internal management of the organization. Since they do not attend services regularly the rabbi or Protestant minister is that fine fellow who sends them an interesting bulletin every week, and they are all for him. Should the leaders call a congregational meeting for the purpose of replacing the clergyman, the majority will nearly always uphold him. Another factor of course is the natural tendency to vote "against the machine," irrespective of the issues involved. The leaders understand this. If they do not like a rabbi, they know they must act quickly.

The auf probe session therefore is full of tension and drama. The leaders are under great pressure, especially if they have already decided to take the new fellow. In such cases they must be very careful in the conduct of the meeting. Being a leader is not all beer and skittles.

The new rabbi is under pressure, too. What to give them? He wonders why they let the other fellow go. Of course he could use the sermon he wrote for his graduation from the seminary. But that doesn't go any more. He tries to feel his way to see if he can find a clue. What to emphasize? Community chest activities? Rotary work? Adult education? Interfaith? Sunday school? Mr. and Mrs. Club? The auf probe rabbi usually takes the intelligent course and comes through with a sermon on the Biblical portion of the week. There is one thing however which he does know: in most of the Protestant churches and Jewish temples of the South today, the leaders are emphasizing one thing very strongly: "Stick to religion—*only*."

After the trial sermon there may be some questions from the floor, and this part of the auf probe session reflects, I think, our most interesting characteristic—ambivalence. It is natural that the folks would like to have a handsome rabbi. On this basis we are no different than all the other peoples of the world. The shaman of the primitive peoples was always the tallest member of the tribe. Eventually when we discovered the uses of intellect we learned how to make up for lack of physical beauty by dressing him in robes, white wigs, purple togas, ermine capes, and miters. Most of the folks in the South, reflecting the attitudes of the dominant society, would like to have a rabbi (you should pardon me) who does not look "too Jewish" (as it has been so often said), yet there is much more to it than that. There is also a terrible longing for the religious and communal culture of their parents and an inherent devotion to the "glories of the past." They want a tall, blue-eyed rabbi, but they also want "a Jewish word," which is a Yiddish colloquialism for "Jewishness" in its deepest sense. What they would really like to have, of course, is Robert Montgomery with "a Jewish word."

Part of this ambivalence is in the theology itself. The members of the Reform congregation, never quite sure that they have done the right thing, want a rabbi with just a smattering of the Orthodox values. The Conservatives, on the other hand, want a rabbi with at least a tinge of the reformer. This often leads to the ambiguity we know so well in our American political structure: Tories who are Democrats and radicals who are Republicans.

And all during the auf probe the ladies are just dying to find out something about the rabbi's wife. They love to have a rabbi's wife of whom they can say, "How sweet," "How self-sacrificing," "She's such a good worker." This means, of

137

course, that the rabbi has a homely wife, which is the ideal situation. A handsome clergyman with a homely wife can practically write his own ticket. But in the early moments of the auf probe the ladies do not even know whether the rabbi is married, and so the smartest of them starts the ball rolling. "Rabbah, do you-all think your wife will like it down heah?" What a brain!

And there are always the people who had been particularly fond of the "resigned" rabbi. In an attempt to demonstrate this loyalty they will make it as hard as they can for the new fellow. On the other hand, the leaders will find it necessary to go all out in their praise. Between these two extremes the new clergyman dares not hope for a smooth inauguration of his ministry.

But after a while the congregation scatters again: the majority reads the weekly bulletin and slowly but surely transfers all past loyalties to the new man; but the leaders take up their vigil: "For the first year we want written committee reports, and please fill in the space under 'co-operation.'" Eventually the new rabbi may even ask for a raise and the leaders sitting around the country club will shake their heads in disbelief: "What does he need an extra five hundred dollars for?" The wives will be sitting at the edge of the swimming pool and will join in: "They have such a cute little house—so near. It's such a charming little place especially since we had those leaks fixed."

And so we'll continue along our interesting path, a dynamic people with a wonderful ambivalence. But if a rabbi in the North is looking for peace and quiet, let him not look toward the Mason-Dixon line.

Werner Pelz

And Cried Bitterly

Whisked at 50 m.p.h. from the bleak Fringedge hills through the deserted Manchester Sunday into the bright green of an early Cheshire spring, I arrived at the lovely old church just in time. It looked dazzlingly clean in the shy sunlight. The vicar's smile floated over a spring cloud of surplice.

The words of exhortation and prayer, the hymns and anthems of the most accomplished choir, flowed like Hymettan honey over four hundred well fed, well clad souls. Colourful millinery blossoms sprouted out of dark undergrowth. At last I stood above them and looked into four hundred slightly upturned faces that did not expect too much. I was reminded of an aerial photograph I had seen the week before of ten or twenty thousand ant-men queueing for their daily soup. I told them about it, for I had been brought all that way to talk about refugees.

I tried to make them smell the squalor, the despair, the apathy, the horror of facing nothing except one's own filth; took them through the camps in the Middle East, the roof dwellings in Hong Kong, the shanty towns of South Africa.

"Our brothers," I said, "so we believe." The beautiful blossoms did not sway under the torrent of words. I bent far over the pulpit to nail them down to their name: "They killed Jesus—whom we call Lord, Lord—because they could not

From *The Guardian* (Manchester), April 18, 1963. Reprinted by permission of the author.

stand a beggar who claimed to possess the secret of life. And he told us that we should find that secret among beggars, among the 'least of his brethren,' the poor in pocket or heart or mind. Only among the poor shall we realise how poor we are. And the poor are promised the kingdom, the earth!" Ekcetera, as we say in Fringedge, ekcetera.

While the soothing recessional gathers momentum, I gaze once more at the subdued stained glass: Christ on a tree, a real tree, rooted in a skull, Adam's skull, in the human brain. "There grows one in the human brain."

Outside, the amazing sun makes us look unreal as we stand about awkwardly in dissolving clusters. The young organist bounces out of the porch, shakes my hand, and says: "You have made them think. That's what they need."

My host takes me in hand. "Those go back to 1500. They have been left almost unchanged." His walking stick points to a double row of houses, mellow and demure in the bright light. "Beautiful." We cross a turf-covered orchard. Every tree looks scrubbed, the bark shiny and silvery—not sooty as in Fringedge. Every tree has a tidy bandage to keep the pest from the fruit that is sure to come. A gently sloping lawn takes us to the grey stone house with wide open, innocent windows.

Inside, we stand round the fire, warming ourselves, floating on a carpet soft as eiderdown. "Mr. Mann has talked to us about refugees," my host says. "He has given us much to think about."

The lady of the house, dressed in most expensive simplicity, still beautiful in her calm, by now perfectly fitting gentility, is sorry she was unable to come: "Our new cook does not yet know her way about the kitchen at all. And Thomas will have to leave us soon after lunch."

Thomas, about 30, is beautifully put together. He reminds me of the trees in the orchard. He stands perfectly still, without a trace of awkwardness. His grey eyes are steadily on me without question or comment. He is the kind of man I envy for his quiet assurance, and love, because I feel the assurance is covering something not altogether sure.

140

"Thomas is a bit of a refugee," says his mother. "He hardly ever sees his London flat. He is responsible for seven works, one in Dundee, one in Southampton, and the others anywhere in between."

Thomas's eyes do not comment. His few words come out of large silences. "Hotels can be rather monotonous. No, thank you, I never drink before dinner."—I do.

"He is very good with the men," his father says, and, at the same time, the lady with the rings on her fingers and a number of necklaces on her taut bosom: "His real home is Glyndebourne. He never misses an opera season there, do you, Thomas? I am sure you are going again this summer." Thomas nods, just perceptibly, with his steady eyelids. "I wish I could. I adore Glyndebourne. But for Thomas it is a spiritual home." For a while the soft curtains and carpets absorb words like Mozart, Bellini, Don Giovanni, Busch, and synonyms of "wonderful."

"It must be a remarkable place," I say. "The only pity that it is so exclusive."

Thomas has not contributed to our starry-eyed conversation. His unemphatic words therefore sound emphatic: "Crowds would spoil it all."

"Have you never been?" my host wants to know, although he knows.

"I shall never be able to afford it, I'm afraid." The brick drops into a pool of silence and all the ripples are left to subside, before Thomas asks: "And how is Fringedge? I used to know it well when I was a boy."

"Probably much as it was when you knew it. It does not change. The railway line still cuts us in two very neatly. On one side live the people with cars and a bit of—culture. On the other, the people who have no cars yet, only television sets and washing machines. And never the twain shall meet."

This seems to be another final remark, so I flounder on: "Only in the morning the one half invades the other across the bridge in the shape of an army of charwomen. Ha ha." No one laughs with me. Their eyes show they want to be polite but

141

don't know how. "This is not a real meeting." I try to grin off my sententiousness.

"Why should they meet?" Thomas breaks the silence so calmly that I could not even hear the question mark.

"It would do us all a lot of good," I say.

"Why." There is no question in the steady eyes and that is why he needs an answer all the more. I also know what I want to say, word for word. But I only stall: "Don't you think that is what the church is there for—breaking the middle wall of partition."

I want to kick myself. "And we have such a lovely parish room." The fire becomes intolerable.

"I don't think it would do any good." I am given another chance. Hic Rhodus—I remember my one Latin tag—hic prophecy. But you cannot prophesy in a drawing room. It sounds so pompous. "I think it is important," I say.

"It would lead to nothing but envy and backbiting. You ought to know. You know what people are like."

I smile a great, big, cynical smile of complicity and contradiction. It can mean "of course I know" or "I know better but shall not argue." Such a big smile that I have to spread my arms, the sherry glass still in my right hand.

The cook rings the bell. I toss down the rest of the sherry as if there weren't a meal I did not start in that way. The sherry gets into my windpipe. For about two minutes I cough and choke. The tears stream down my cheeks. I feel utterly alone, surrounded by the silence of that perfect breeding which treats as non-existent an agony it feels—quite rightly—to be slightly indecent.

Catholic Parlor Game

Early addicts of this department will recall an item published last December, describing a staff member's suggestion of a game that would corner the Catholic market. We quote: "His idea—which we hereby copyright lest somebody act on it—envisions a game modeled on Monopoly ('Outside the Church no salvation') with a title borrowed from Bishop Sheen: 'Go to Heaven.' Each of the dice has a drop of Lourdes water inside it. You roll the dice, then move your piece of soul around the board, encountering occasions of sin, accumulating indulgences. If you roll a pair you have to pick up a Mystery Card. The card may read: 'You have been made a Monsignor. Move back five spaces.' Or: 'You have died in agony as a martyr. Go directly to Heaven. Do not stop at Purgatory.' "

Well. It now appears that we were too late, and, further, that truth is wilder than imagination. A game called "Merit" was copyrighted in 1962, and an ad in last April's *Specialty Salesman* urged potential salesmen to:

"MINT MONEY WITH THIS 100% PROFIT Whirlwind Religious Educational Seller!"

The game, says the ad, "TEACHES CHILDREN and ADULTS CATHOLICISM THE EASY, FUN WAY!" "Get Ready for Peak Easter, First Communion & Confirmation Sales!" "IT'S THE ONLY TEACHING AID OF ITS KIND WITH ECCLESIASTICAL APPROBATION."

From *The National Catholic Reporter* (Kansas City, Mo.), July 14, 1965. Reprinted by permission of the publisher.

A Laugh at the Laity

The approbation, according to the rule book, comes from the Most Rev. Bernard J. Topel of Spokane.

We don't expect to be able to convey the entire mystique of the Merit game, but it goes something like this. At the start each player is issued 700 Merits, a card certifying his baptism and a statuette. You get to move your statuette around the board by correctly answering questions, and depending on which space you land on, you gain or sacrifice Merits, help build church properties, and acquire sacraments. To win you have to have six of the seven sacraments, retain or regain 700 Merits and return Home. Nobody can win, however, till all six properties (church, convent, school, seminary, Catholic Charities and Foreign Missions) have been built. But the Foreign Missions can't be built till the convent and seminary are built, just as St. Paul taught.

All right, let's say you've got your infant of Prague or Sacred Heart statuette, you've been baptized and it's your turn. Here are some questions you might draw from the question deck:

"Q. Is it wrong to neglect confirmation? A. Yes, it is a sin to neglect confirmation. *If answered correctly move 4 spaces.*"

"Q. What kind of sorrow should we have for our sins? A. The sorrow we should have for our sins should be interior, supernatural, universal, and sovereign. *If answered correctly move 3 spaces.*"

"Q. Is our confession worthy if we cannot remember the number of our sins? A. Yes, but we should tell the number as nearly as possible. *If answered correctly move 5 spaces.*"

Let's say you've answered a 6-space question correctly; you land on a Merit space and get to draw from the Merit deck. Sample Merit cards:

"Today You Remembered Never to Tell or Laugh at Smutty Stories. *25 Merits.*"

"You Have Been Entirely Honest in All Your Dealings. *50 Merits.*"

"You Made a Two-Day Retreat. *100 Merits.*"

144

On the other hand, you might have moved only four spaces and landed on a Sacrifice space. Sample Sacrifice cards: "You Have Become a Case for Catholic Charities, if You Are Past Catholic Charities Return There and Donate Five Merits . . . If You Are Not Yet There Donate Them Five Merits . . . Do This Whether It Is Built or Not."

If you land on the Fund Raiser space everybody else has to contribute a couple hundred Merits or so to build the church or convent or whatever else needs building. There is also a space for each sacrament. You can't have both Holy Orders and Matrimony, but apparently little girl players can be ordained. Even if ordained, a player gets 100 Merits every time he passes Home for saying the Family Rosary.

The ad in *Specialty Salesman* says that sales in a test period in Spokane reached $131,600. And no wonder. Nowhere else could you learn that the sixth commandment forbids "adultry," that the Good Thief was named "Dismus," or that "On Holy Saturday there is no Mass said and Holy Communion is not given." Moreover, the price to salesmen is $6.50, to the customer $12.50.

And, as the ad says, "If you sell educational courses, encyclopedias, children's books, records, bibles, shoes, vacuum cleaners or cosmetics—here's a sure and easy way to give yourself a pay raise. Merit is the perfect door opener, premium, extra money maker."

"Best of all," says the clincher, "Merit is genuine family entertainment, full of laughter, excitement and competitive fun. Everyone will *beg* to play the *only* game ever to receive Ecclesiastical Approbation."

Bernard Basset, S.J.

Celia's Engagement

Ours, I suppose, was a good Catholic home. We certainly had fish on Fridays, the definitive sign for the average Englishman of those who have sold their soul to Rome. In fact, we went much further than fish. If all our prayerbooks had been placed head to tail, they would have stretched to Jerusalem, while the statuary in our combined bedrooms gave us a status second only to Madame Tussaud's.

With only one crucifix and a solitary prayerbook, I was judged by the children to be very Low Church. Margery boasted a brace of miraculous Madonnas, a portrait of Christ painted in ecstasy by a Portuguese sister, a candle carried by Pope Leo XIII on some famous occasion and a reliquary which would have made Chaucer smile. The children took after their mother in piety if not in taste. Their statues were luminous and plastic, of a style often associated with souvenir shops on the Margate esplanade. They loved these garish reproductions and I doubt if Our Lady is fussy about art. Despite the ecclesiastical bric-a-brac in the bedrooms I used, at one time, to worry about our faith. Lying on the floor each day, absorbed in the mystery of the Divine Presence, I wondered how I could teach my children to pray. The practice of the presence of God seemed so essential that I would have loved to have had them all lying on their backs.

From *We Neurotics* by Bernard Basset, New York: Herder & Herder, Inc., 1963. Reprinted by permission of the publisher.

Margery scotched the suggestion with an unkind reference to poor Mr. Owles. The Canon blanched when I asked him and, though he wrapped up his answer in polite, theological jargon, he made it very clear that my methods were too odd. Fr Mulligatawny, the curate, was hot on the family rosary; he begged me not to worry so much about the mystery of the Trinity but to entrust my family daily to the great Mother of God. Miss Copsley-Smith, dispensing enormous gins, thought that every soul must find its own level and that a little casual agnosticism never did a teenager any harm. Lastly, the Little Nun wrote to say that piety was family feeling towards God. She was quite certain that my children had it and that on no account should it be artificially produced.

Contemplation was, therefore, off and, in its place, we tried the family rosary without much success. The telephone intervened three times in four decades and in the muddle I forgot the title of the fifth. There was general giggling and the boys sent my name to the Catholic Enquiry Centre for a postal course. So ended my efforts to make my family godly; with some sorrow we reverted to laissez-faire.

In so many devout books written for Christian parents, authors take it for granted that Mum or Dad gather the children round them for a heart to heart talk. This never happened or looked like happening in our home. Once the children had gone to boarding school, Margery and I were forced into the background and rarely dared to assert our views in matters of faith. Either Fr X or Mother St Y were quoted against us and we found ourselves under instruction from the boys. Margery, bolder than I and convent-trained, might occasionally deliver a talk on Christian behaviour but the children would laugh and call out for silence "as Mummy is going to give a homily!" I kept myself to myself. Margery said that I had let her down, that I was ashamed to profess my faith before my children and she even employed the "let us ask Daddy" technique. It was safer not to speak. I could manage a factual discussion on the number of Cardinals in the Roman curia but, when it came to purity, confession or communion, a painful embarrassment settled on us all. These cosy chats set out so sympathetically in the pamphlets proved hopelessly out of place in our blasphemous house. Should one feel so awkward in speaking to one's children about the dearest and most important facts of life? I used to lie on the floor and pray for an enlightenment which was never granted; shyness triumphed on either side.

The children were unreliable but never bad. We used to have a liturgical spell with Dominus Vobiscums ringing round the bathroom as Harry and Benjamin practised for High Mass. After playing priests day and night for a week, the liturgy was discarded and God gave way to the Australian cricket tour. On one vacation, Celia went all godly after a term in Mother Mary of the Holy Trinity's class. Celia spoke in a religious whisper and, when asked what was the matter by her mother, announced that she was making reparation for the sins of the world. She was going to be a nun at the time but, by the next vacation, her very soul would swoon for jazz. Elvis Presley, or whoever it was, dislodged St. Aloysius and the nearest that we came to contemplation was a recording of Bing Crosby singing "Bless This House." My only chance of speaking about religion was when the boys were short of cash. They would have borne long extracts from *The Ascent of Mount Carmel* to get half-a-crown. If piety is family feeling towards God, I could cease from worry; they treated God much as they treated Margery and me.

There were the usual difficulties. At one time Harry ran up debts in secret, Benjamin turned secretive, Celia sprawled in a sofa reading romantic magazines. Or they would tease Betty, their little sister, and she would run to me. Celia at sixteen was crazy about dancing and some of the dances to which she was invited seemed to Margery very advanced. Celia informed me of one such dance that Mother Mary of the Trinity approved entirely and that all the proceeds were to go to a leper colony outside Singapore. If the end could justify the means in such exalted circles, Margery and I could only shut our eyes and

148

Bernard Basset, S.J.: *Celia's Engagement*

pray. We prayed for the children every day but, save for fish on Fridays, could do little else.

In due course the boys left school for university and three years later Celia was an undergraduate reading botany with infectious zest. She was now the image of her mother as I had known her twenty-five years before. This physical bond proved often irresistible and from the age of sixteen onwards Celia, more than any of the others, made our home. She was motherly to me, endlessly patient, always sympathetic; we shared a love of poetry and music and a lively interest in little people, their foibles, heartbreaks, hobbies, attitudes to life. She would bounce into the drawingroom, laughing, to tell me of the secondhand car that some friends were buying, of the lecturer's poodle who yawned during his master's lecture, of a Parsee graduate who had proposed to her. She was very pretty, refreshingly happy, industrious and kind. Our daily routine went on peacefully without her but her comings and goings, her friends, her rags, her dresses, dances and expeditions set the interest and pattern for our lives.

Celia had been at the University for two years and seemed deeply committed when Margery informed me tearfully that our daughter wanted to become a nun. The girl had not said this in so many words but, when Margery was pressing for information about her boy friends, Celia's noncommittal answers had served as a warning and a clue. Margery could only hope that she was wrong, she advised me not to say anything about it, she begged me to mark her words.

I could not help smiling for while Margery and I in the olden days had often discussed the unlikely honour of a priest or nun in our family, we had never wanted God to take this too seriously. The quest for a suitable husband for her daughter lies at the centre of a mother's thoughts. Margery had never said so, but I knew very well that she saw in Celia's future marriage the prolongation of her own maternal life.

To me even the hint of a possible vocation to religion came as a sickening shock. According to all the holy books, I should have greeted the news with a heartfelt Alleluja, for can there be a higher favour than this? Yet doubts pressed in on every side and mounted until I felt both resentful and rebellious towards God. It became increasingly hard to lie on the floor, more and more difficult to submit to God as a father, less and less certain whether I believed in His existence at all. In public no hint was given, but I found myself watching Celia with pain and incredulity, wondering how a girl so affectionate could plot in secret to dash all her parents' hopes.

Why was I so distressed? I had to recognise the fact that Celia at twenty-one could do what she wished with her life. I could not stop her from being a nun any more than I could prevent her from marrying a Parsee if she wished to or of living in San Francisco should she so choose. I would, one day, lose her anyway. On the other hand, if she entered a convent we would have to visit her and sit in a gloomy parlour; she would never enter her home again. They would dress my Celia up in linen blinkers and pick for her, out of the litany of saints, some high-falutin' name. A further, more painful doubt assailed me as to whether priests and nuns were so much better than men and women working in the world? I must not weary you with my morbid misgivings all of which seem so ridiculous now. Behind all these bitter thoughts lay a far more terrifying problem, was I so sure that there was a God? Lying on the floor, striving for peace, adoring God as a step to sanity, were these sufficient proofs of His existence, arguments strong enough for me to allow my beloved daughter to waste her life? Ours may not have been a very edifying home, but Celia's vocation was surely based on my behaviour over so many years. She believed in God and her faith was untroubled because mine had seemed so secure.

It is never easy to obtain advice on so personal a subject for there would be special pleading on either side. The Canon was ex officio prejudiced in favour of vocations while Fr Mulligatawny already had three sister nuns. On the other side, most of my friends, even the Catholics, would condemn such a stultifying step. Nuns are only fashionable in Britain when they quit their cloister for the world. My friends would agree that God is all very well in heaven, but it is carrying belief a little too far when a pretty girl squanders her life for Him. Margery herself would not put it this way but if I had doubts about it, I could presume a similar state of misgiving even in her.

In the end and with considerable hesitation I decided not to look for advice. Instead, I turned up the passage of Genesis to read about Abraham and Isaac for it dawned on me that this ancient patriarch, far out in the desert, faced a similar issue to myself. It was an effort to lie on the floor. Here indeed was a test; in cold blood and with every personal interest pulling against it, to make an act of faith. Leaving Celia's decision aside, for she was in this her own master, was I prepared to accept her departure for the sake of a God who had come to me, lying on the ground? Here was a heart-rending choice between the absorbing physical love of my own daughter and an intangible awe towards a being, always invisible, who meant nothing physical to me at all.

Well, Celia went to her convent. She finished her degree with a glorious burst, sparkled with love for us both in what I knew was her last summer holiday with us and then told me as we paced the sand dunes outside Burnham that she thought that she would like to be a nun. The shyness of former days remained. We said very little to each other, we agreed in a general way that this was a very great honour, that we would miss each other very much. I took it as a compliment when Margery later told me in tears that I was heartless and that even Celia had been astonished that I seemed so genuinely pleased.

"Pleased" is too slight a word. Is there any word in any language to express the relief after a cold-blooded act of faith? I had felt, lying on the floor, that friendship grows painful and embarrassing with all the giving from one side. Celia was not mine to give—doubtless she would have gone without me— but I shared with Abraham the supreme satisfaction that consent was mine. God could never mean to me as much as did

151

Celia but, in one glorious moment, I was determined to show that I loved Him more.

Celia is very happy in her convent and, maybe, part of her strange contentment stems from an act of surrender similar to mine. Hers, I think, was the easier part for she now has a multitude of schemes, exhibitions, offices, employments, a lovely black habit to help her feel holy and a monster rosary clanking by her side. She tells me that it often reminds her of our famous family rosary which ended in gales of laughter so many years ago.

Margery is, now, very proud and moves with the majesty of a Reverend Mother; I, too, am contented to have it so. But the God who fills the heavens and will one day reward us, is still not able to fill Celia's empty room.

Part Five:

Scattered Shots

The selections that follow would not fit comfortably within any of the preceding parts. Their targets vary, their methods diverge. Together they illustrate the wide range of possibilities open to the religious satirist.

When C. S. LEWIS wrote *The Screwtape Letters* in 1942, during the Battle of Britain, they immediately became popular in church, seminary, and literary circles. Lewis, an Oxbridge teacher of medieval literature, was recognized as an urbane Christian apologist whose style went far beyond mere cleverness. He succeeded in raising satire to a level of argumentation, hard logic, and conviction. His writings are examples of that satire which at the same time becomes a vehicle for constructive theological witness. SEAN O'CASEY, who has so often and so splendidly displayed his talents as dramatist and essayist, gives us a rumination about all that has gone on in history to account for the fact that a young Protestant boy should be dragged off by the ears to a dour classroom of a church school. The studied seriousness of the historical causes and antecedents, with the understated humor, reminds one very much of

153

Mark Twain. ROBERT NATHAN, whose satirical style has been characterized as that of "tossing his characters on his two-forked prong of pitying wit," portrays the fight for the human soul. No stridency or maliciousness spoils Nathan's civilized wit. This chapter gives only clues and hints as to his final purpose. His book should be read in its entirety. ROBERT MCAFEE BROWN, Protestant teacher of theology, knows the use and misuse to which the Bible has been put. He is quick to suggest additional possibilities for exploitation of "the Book of Books," whose authority in religion and influence in history are unparalleled. ANTHONY TOWNE, religious journalist, brings the collection to a close by administering a hot-foot to theological faddism. Announcements as startling as "God is dead" leave even the avant-garde bewildered. The funeral rites, which were proclaimed more persuasively in other ages by Thomas Hardy, Friedrich Nietszche, and others, are here exposed to the withering literalism the contemporary announcers invite.

C. S. Lewis

The Clarity Hell Affords

[*Note: Wormwood is a junior devil, subordinate to his uncle and advisor, the satanic sycophant Screwtape. The "Enemy" is God.*]

My Dear Wormwood,

I note with grave displeasure that your patient has become a Christian. Do not indulge the hope that you will escape the usual penalties; indeed, in your better moments, I trust you would hardly even wish to do so. In the meantime we must make the best of the situation. There is no need to despair; hundreds of these adult converts have been reclaimed after a brief sojourn in the Enemy's camp and are now with us. All the *habits* of the patient, both mental and bodily, are still in our favour.

One of our great allies at present is the Church itself. Do not misunderstand me. I do not mean the Church as we see her spread out through all time and space and rooted in eternity, terrible as an army with banners. That, I confess, is a spectacle which makes our boldest tempters uneasy. But fortunately it is quite invisible to these humans. All your patient sees is the half-finished, sham Gothic erection on the new building estate. When he goes inside, he sees the local grocer with rather an oily expression on his face bustling up to offer him one shiny

little book containing a liturgy which neither of them under-
stands, and one shabby little book containing corrupt texts of a
number of religious lyrics, mostly bad, and in very small print.
When he gets to his pew and looks round him he sees just that
selection of his neighbours whom he has hitherto avoided. You
want to lean pretty heavily on those neighbours. Make his
mind flit to and fro between an expression like "the body of
Christ" and the actual faces in the next pew. It matters very
little, of course, what kind of people that next pew really
contains. You may know one of them to be a great warrior on
the Enemy's side. No matter. Your patient, thanks to Our
Father below, is a fool. Provided that any of those neighbours
sing out of tune, or have boots that squeak, or double chins, or
odd clothes, the patient will quite easily believe that their
religion must therefore be somehow ridiculous. At his present
stage, you see, he has an idea of "Christians" in his mind which
he supposes to be spiritual but which, in fact, is largely
pictorial. His mind is full of togas and sandals and armour and
bare legs and the mere fact that the other people in church
wear modern clothes is a real—though of course an unconscious—difficulty to him. Never let it come to the surface;
never let him ask what he expected them to look like. Keep
everything hazy in his mind now, and you will have all
eternity wherein to amuse yourself by producing in him the
peculiar kind of clarity which Hell affords.

Work hard, then, on the disappointment or anticlimax
which is certainly coming to the patient during his first few
weeks as a churchman. The Enemy allows this disappointment
to occur on the threshold of every human endeavour. It occurs
when the boy who has been enchanted in the nursery by
Stories from the Odyssey buckles down to really learning
Greek. It occurs when lovers have got married and begin the
real task of learning to live together. In every department of
life it marks the transition from dreaming aspiration to laborious doing. The Enemy takes this risk because He has a curious
fantasy of making all these disgusting little human vermin into
what He calls His "free" lovers and servants—"sons" is the

156

word He uses, with His inveterate love of degrading the whole spiritual world by unnatural liaisons with the two-legged animals. Desiring their freedom, He therefore refuses to carry them, by their mere affections and habits, to any of the goals which He sets before them: He leaves them to "do it on their own". And there lies our opportunity. But also, remember, there lies our danger. If once they get through this initial dryness successfully, they become much less dependent on emotion and therefore much harder to tempt.

I have been writing hitherto on the assumption that the people in the next pew afford no *rational* ground for disappointment. Of course if they do—if the patient knows that the woman with the absurd hat is a fanatical bridgeplayer or the man with squeaky boots a miser and an extortioner—then your task is so much the easier. All you then have to do is to keep out of his mind the question "If I, being what I am, can consider that I am in some sense a Christian, why should the different vices of those people in the next pew prove that their religion is mere hypocrisy and convention?" You may ask whether it is possible to keep such an obvious thought from occurring even to a human mind. It is, Wormwood, it is! Handle him properly and it simply won't come into his head. He has not been anything like long enough with the Enemy to have any real humility yet. What he says, even on his knees, about his own sinfulness is all parrot talk. At bottom, he still believes he has run up a very favourable credit-balance in the Enemy's ledger by allowing himself to be converted, and thinks that he is showing great humility and condescension in going to church with these "smug", commonplace neighbours at all. Keep him in that state of mind as long as you can.

Your affectionate uncle

SCREWTAPE

Sean O'Casey

The Protestant Kid
Thinks of the Reformation

So, with his hands and face washed and a clean collar round his neck, Johnny was lugged off to school beside his mother, with the Reverend Hunter walking a little in front.

What past-gone long-gone dog-gone thing had bred this dragging of him along at the backside of this soft-hatted stiff-collared chancer to be fitted in to the life of a protestant day school? Maybe because Moses had stopped to have a gawk at the burning bush; or that the Israelites were able to make mincemeat of the Amalekites; or that the followers of Christ were first called Christians at Antioch; or, maybe, it was really because of

The Protestant Reformation.

In the sixteenth century the simple and pure gospel handed down by the apostles was, without doubt, in its last gasp and ready to go bang at any minute, which, had it happened, would have deprived us of the great peace, security, and freedom that Christians enjoy at the present day. The pope, cardinals, bishops, and priests, far from following after goodness and orderly conversation, were rushing round every-where on palfreys, jennets, mules, and chargers, looking for thrills, and jack-acting in festive season and sad season, as if they, and they only, had a special permit to shake a lot of merriment out of life. Black friars, white friars, purple-hooded monks, brown-caped priests, crimson-cassocked cardinals, and mitred abbots were eating the people out of house and home, and there wasn't a sign to be seen anywhere that heaven was any the better for the taxing and tithing that went on without let or hindrance everywhere. Rags, bones, and bottles, framed in precious stones, were carried about in holy processions, and were honoured and venerated by the mutt-massed people. The holy college of cardinals was turning out saints by steam, and there were so many of them that if a man wanted to say Pray for me to each one of them, he would have to keep going hard for ten hours a day, without a break for breakfast, dinner, or tea, and even then, according to an unquestionable ecclesiastical authority, it would take him three hundred and sixty-five thousand years to get near the end of the litany, so that there was small chance of God getting a look-in in the way of hearing Himself talked about, and praised by His people.

It was commonly reported by those who were close up to the inner circle, that, if a monk was to be kept from straddling a judy, he had to be shut up in a stone coffin, and let out only under the supervision of a hundred halberdiers while he was having a snack in the first, second, and third watches of the day, but as this guardianship of the ladies was too costly and too troublesome, the monks had it all their own way, and there wasn't a lassie in the whole wide world who didn't know a codpiece from the real thing, even when her eyes were shut and her mind wandering. And if any man made as much as a murmur, he was hit on the head with an excommunication that sent him falling headlong down to hell, without the slightest chance throughout all eternity of ever touching the bottom, with the tortures getting worse every foot he fell, and the power to feel them getting stronger every second it took to fall an inch further, while, all the time, the poor tumbling soul was flushed with the remembrance that some monk was working overtime in an enjoyment that should have been his alone.

159

So the poor people were worn out trying to think of a change that would bring them a little less of the next world and a little more of this, and they secretly cried to God, and their prayers must have been heard, for during this time, or thereabouts, an Augustine monk stuck in the monastery of Wittenberg began to turn over the leaves of the Book of Books, the Bible, that was anchored to a big-bellied desk with a heavy chain so that the Book of Books couldn't be stolen by those unable to read or write. And this monk, who was called Luther, read and read by sunlight, moonlight, starlight, and candlelight, till he was nearly blind, and he was greatly aston-ished at what he read therein, for it wasn't a bit like anything he had read himself, or had heard read by anyone else, it was all so good, so bad, so reading on and reading ever, he prayed when he was puzzled, and reviewed in his mind all that had been written, and all that had been preached aforetime about the heavens and hell, the earth and all that was under the earth, the sea and all that in it is, till he got to know just where he was standing, and found out that there were differences here and differences there which wouldn't bear investigation, and had a dangerous tendency to deceive and corrupt innocent, simple, and stupid people who were anxious to serve God in spirit and in truth to the best of their ability, so long as they could get bread from heaven in a less laborious way and at a reasonable price.

So Luther thumped his breast, saying as he thumped it hard and heavy, am I right or am I wrong? And a voice so still and small, that Luther could hardly hear it, answered out of the light, so loud and shrill that it nearly burst the drum of his ear, each voice sounding together though they spoke at different times saying, Get busy, man, and teach the truth of the gospel, for out of the teaching and the truth will come swarms of fighting men, beating of drums and blowing of bugles, big guns and little guns, and great ships of war, so that red men, yellow men, and black men will become, in course of time, the white man's lawful god-fearing and most obedient batmen.

And Luther rose up like a giant refreshed, and after heart-

searching and mind-searching and soul-searching, he saw
clearly that the one thing the church thought of was the
laying-up of a lot for a rainy day, which was repugnant to the
plain words of holy scripture, thereby causing an undue delay
to the great multitude of souls that waddled and squirmed and
shuffled along on the road to Mandalay where the gates of
heaven lay.

So Luther told the simple people that they'd simply got to
give up obeying rules and regulations, and use their own
judgment about whatsoever things were true, whatsoever
things were honest, whatsoever things were just, whatsoever
things were lovely, whatsoever things were of good report,
and to decide themselves as to what things to believe, what
things to say, and what things to do, using the Bible, and only
the Bible, as the general store of knowledge of what was and is
and is to come.

But the popes and priests opened into a full stride of
opposition, and they argued with him and fought him and
persecuted him and tried in every way to double-cross and
crucify him, but Luther stood firm to the shock in his smock
like a rock and mocked them with many words, and laughed in
their raging faces, telling them that they'd have to get up early
in the morning, if they wanted him to sit still and sing dumb.
So Luther kept thundering out the truth as it came straight
from God, and the princes and many rich merchants who
lived only for the truth as it is in Christ Jesus and was in
Luther, and who scorned to do a wrong thing to their neigh-
bour, in business or out of business, rallied and tallied and
dallied and sallied round the doughty reformer, and cheered
him up, and told him that the Lord was a very present help in
time of trouble, so that Luther believed and spit on his hands
and said, Let them all come, and he was made strong and hefty
in his going in and going out and in his arguments from that
very hour.

Then Luther decided to let things rip, and went at it,
hammer and tongs, and made short work of the traffic of
indulgences, a gilt-edged superstition that let anyone do any-

thing from pitch-and-toss to manslaughter, so long as a suitable fee was dropped in the back pocket in the pants of a priest. And the big princes and little princes, margraves and mere-graves, landgraves and landgrieves, and merchants in gold and silver and silks, and merchants in ebony and ivory and coffee and tea, drew their swords, and cheered Luther on, shouting, Go on, Martin, old boy, in the name o' God, and give them socks and cut the bowels out of them, and show them we know the Lord is our God who is gracious and merciful, and high above all nations, and prove to them that souls that are pure and simple have only to skim a few texts from the Bible to know all things, and to know how to deal justly with men present and men past and men to come, and your name will be a banner and a shout and a buckler to generations of popery-purged protestants as long as the sun shall move and the earth stand still.

Then Luther got excited, and showed, by miles and miles of documentary evidence, that the most secret sayings which puzzled archangels could be easily understood of the veriest babes and sucklings, so long as they really wanted to know what was the truth and what wasn't the truth, as it was written aforetime by the holy apostles and prophets.

But the Devil getting anxious about his status, stirred up the hearts of the pope, cardinals, abbots, and abbesses to anger, and they made bloody war on all who were determined to follow the commandments of God in a pure and simple way, and many fierce battles were fought between the followers of God on the one hand, and the followers of Satan on the other, so that thousands on both sides were slain in an effort to keep the Christian church from perishing.

But Luther, at peace with God and himself, went on purify-ing and surifying and curifying and furifying the Christian faith so that the frightened red-hatted cardinals, looking out of high windows, saw the people happily going by, and saw the people looking up to see all heaven opened up to them, and the cardinals were sore afraid in their hearts. When they saw this busy traffic of true worship going on, night and day, without

162

let or hindrance, and heard the people singing heart to heart honest to God hymns, they hastened to hide behind the curtains, and wist not what to do.

And the truth, the whole truth, and nothing but the truth, so help me God, spread like lightning, and came with a great flush and rush and gush to such as those who had nothing else to do but to look for it, so that the people in millions queued up to read the Bible, with their kids, and while the parents read the Book of Books, the kids went swing-swong on the chains that bound the Bibles to the desks, so that the lives of the people began to bubble-bible up and bible-bubble over with beauty and a singular blessedness, for all their hearts were filled with peace.

And it came to pass that the anger of those who possessed not the truth was kindled against those who had it, and a great dispute arose about the word, whence it came and where it stayed and whither it went, so that each fell upon the other in a fierce fight that has lasted down to this very day. And such as were taken captive by those who had not the truth, had their right hands cut off and their noses sliced up, and were burned at the stake with their heads up; but those who had the truth showed mercy unto their captives, for they cut off their left hands only, sliced down their noses, and burned them at the stake with their heads down, so that they died more quickly.

So the reformation came wholly to England and partly to Ireland, bringing with it the Bible and a burning love of truth, love, peace, righteousness, joy, and fair dealing along straight paths and round corners. And England went from strength to strength and from power to power, having the finest army in the world, and the greatest navy in the world, and the biggest budgets in the world, and the wisest statesmen in the world, and she set out and conquered many races, taming the wild ones with love and great tact, so that red men and black men and yellow men came and ate quietly out of her hand and all these things were done that it might be fulfilled, which was spoken by the prophets about those wondrous ones who never

163

lost their love for or steadfast faith in the Book of Books, the Bible.

A wave or two of the truth as it was in Luther splashed over Ireland, and so in process of time, The Reverend Hunter was born in protestant circumstances that make him a sky-pilot, and Johnny was born a protestant in circumstances that placed him in the position of being lugged along at the backside of this soft-hatted stiff-collared egg-headed oul' henchman of heaven, to be added to his swarm of urchins cowering and groping about in the rag-and-bone education provided by the church and state for the children of those who hadn't the wherewithal to do anything better.

Hunter, Johnny, and his mother came to the gate of the school.

—In you go, said Hunter, and, if you try hard enough to be a good boy, you'll succeed, and God will bless you.

Off the spiritual pirate toddled, and Johnny and his mother faced forward to the gloom of the doorway leading to the inner gloom of the school.

Robert Nathan

The Devil with Love

Lucifer, the great Archangel, stood in awful majesty upon the highest pinnacle of Hell. The fallen Seraph, folded in his immense wings as in a cloak of darkness, gazed with somber eyes at the demons ranged around him, who returned his look with apprehension. His expression, naturally lofty and severe, was even more critical than usual.

Below him, in Limbo, waited the uneasy souls of the unbaptized and unredeemed: there, for the first time, ancient man saw his descendants. There the Mousterian and the Aurignacian confronted each other, and the Neanderthal gazed in awe at the artist of the cave-paintings of the Dordogne. Arrayed in terrible armour the hosts of the Sumerians, Egyptians, Chaldeans, Persians, Greeks, Scythians, Parthians, and early Romans maneuvered for advantage, while the armies of Attila and Genghis Khan moved like locusts across the empty plain.

They could be forgiven because they had never known any better. The damned were still further down, in pits of molten fire—in particular those heretics who had rebelled against Mother Church. Among them were the Albigensians and the Cathars; the Cathars in particular were indignant at what had happened to them.

In the very lowest pits of all were thrown those souls who

had sinned against the Devil himself, by attempting to outdo him in evil. Here were to be found such characters as the Marquis de Sade, Bluebeard, and Dr. Crippen. However, his greatest indignation was reserved for those who denied God. "It is all very well to defy Him, as I do," he declared, "but it's quite another thing to deny His existence! To do so is to deny my own—for where would I be without that great and shining Adversary?"

"I believe that you love him!" exclaimed Beelzebub in surprise.

Lucifer made a gesture of impatience. "I don't love Him," he said; "I adore Him. But you can't expect me to change my nature."

He went on to explain that his nature was proud, rebellious, and acquisitive. "I am a collector," he said, and looked around him proudly. Just the same, he realized that Hell was becoming crowded beyond its capacity; and gazing downward to where ever fresh multitudes were entering through the gates, he remarked with a sigh:

"Really, I am up to my . . ."

At that moment, catching sight of the delicious shades of Francesca da Rimini and Madame de Pompadour strolling nearby, he stopped himself in mid-sentence, made a leg, and continued in altered tones:

"We have too many souls here."

Asmodeus, who was standing beside him, exclaimed at this evidence of refinement. But Lucifer continued:

"As a matter of fact, I have thought for a long time that we are going about this the wrong way. A soul is such an immaterial thing, it is unworldly, it does nothing while on earth, and can be said to exist only here or in Heaven. And it is so easily caught, besides: one has only to be observant, and quick, and to get there before the priest. While on the other hand, the human heart . . . ah, my friends, that is a horse of another color, that is what gets things done. The heart beats in the world, and creates empires and dynasties; it is the greatest architect of history. Where else will you find the loftiest

166

dreams combined with the most childish anxieties? And what else gives birth to charity, to orphanages and foundations, and to crimes of every kind, as well as the most beautiful symphonies and love stories?"

He gazed around him with a gloomy expression. "Who has won the most hearts?" he asked. "Ourselves—or You-Know-Who? We have a thousand souls to His one; but on earth as in Heaven, He gets the love."

Lilith, who was in the group surrounding him, gave a voluptuous sigh. "Love," she said. And she gazed hopefully at a famous motion-picture star, who returned her gaze in a confused manner. His arm was linked with hat of Alcibiades, the son of Clineas, the Athenian.

The great Archangel strode up and down, pondering. "It is much easier to hate than to love," he said at last. "To hate is to exclude, to love is to accept, to draw in . . . which calls for a different set of muscles. To say No is to finish something; to say Yes is to begin it. I wish I had hearts to love me, on earth."

At this, one of the surrounding shades stepped eagerly forward. He wore his hair in a curving bang over his forehead, and had a small mustache directly beneath his nose. Holding out his arm in a stiff salute, he exclaimed,

"*Sieg Heil!*"

"*Heil*," said Lucifer.

"My Leader," cried the shade. "Let us not bother our heads about love, which is only for cowards and Jews! We are all heroes here. Hate! That is the thing! Let us have our hearts filled with hate, as we had at home!"

So saying, he stepped back, with a satisfied air.

"Thank you, Adolf," said Lucifer.

"It is nothing."

"No," admitted Lucifer sadly, "it is nothing."

It was agreed that something must be done, that a new evangel should be sent to earth to buy men's hearts rather than their souls. But there was no agreement as to how this mission should be organized, or who was to head it; for every lost soul

167

was convinced, just as he had been on earth, that he was right
and everybody else was wrong. There were outcries, and some
hair-pulling; and several fist fights developed, particularly
among those whose lives had been devoted to politics, or
musical criticism.

In the end—as he had expected—Lucifer was obliged to
make up his own mind. Calling to his side the Archdemon
Samael of Hod, he addressed him in the elevated style that he
reserved for such occasions.

"We have been together a long time, dear friend," he said;
"as long as I can remember. For you were one of the original
band who shared with me those glorious days among the
Cherubs and with my brothers, the Seraphim, before disaster
overtook us. In fact, you are considered in the *Bahir*, or
Yerushalmi of the Kabalah, to have been the one who accosted
Eve, riding upon a serpent or a camel, depending upon the
vowel points. Ah me! Those regions of light and joy! I know
that you, too, think of them with regret."

Samael, who had heard Lucifer speak in this vein before,
looked anxiously at his master. What is coming now? he
thought.

The fallen Seraph continued:

"Now hear this. I have chosen you, Samael of Hod, to
undertake a great—and possibly last—mission to the world,
since it is possible that man will blow himself up very shortly,
thereby wiping himself off the face of the earth. The thought
of being obliged to court the cockroaches—who may be all
that is left—depresses me. I want to gather a few men's hearts,
as many as possible, while there is still time."

"Oh," said Samael, "that's it."

"Women too?"

"Certainly," said Lucifer, somewhat surprised. "Women
too. Why not?"

The corners of Samael's mouth drew down. "They have
always been troublemakers," he declared. "My head still aches
from being stepped on in the Garden; I can still hear those

awful words: "It shall bruise thy head and thou shalt bruise his heel."

"Nevertheless," said Lucifer. He laid a kindly arm around Samael's shoulder. "As far as headaches go," he said, "don't forget that I fell a long ways, too."

"Who could forget it?" asked Samael glumly.

Lucifer then told him that he had just received an offer from the United States of America. "It comes from a Mr. Alfred Sneeden," he said, "a resident of the town of Parish, in the county of the same name. I believe that Parish, however, is not the county seat. Mr. Sneeden desires youth, and a certain young lady named Gladys Milhouser. Remember the name. He offers the usual . . . I want you to arrange to take his heart instead."

The demon gave Lucifer a piteous look. "Do I have to?" he asked.

Lucifer inclined his head.

"If only it weren't the United States," said Samael with a sigh. "It is up to its . . ."

"Careful," said Lucifer. "There are ladies present."

"It is full of evangelists," said Samael weakly.

"There is a difference," said Lucifer. "We don't ask for contributions."

Still with his arm around Samael's shoulder, and spreading his dark, enormous wings, Lucifer flew to a side door, which he opened with an iron key. A blast of icy cold struck Samael in the face. Turning, he looked back for a moment at the warm firelight, the billowing clouds stained by the glow of sulphurous fires, the bustle and clatter of Hell. "Geronimo!" he cried; and taking a deep breath, stepped out into space.

"Good luck," said Lucifer. "Keep us posted."

Robert McAfee Brown

Making the Bible Relevant

An enterprising publisher recently issued *The Teen-Age Version of the Holy Bible.* I expected to find Holy Writ in a contemporary idiom ("And God leveled with the Israelite kids, saying, 'Get with it, chums!'"). All we got, however, was the old King James Version with minimal changes for clarity. Frankly, it's hard to see how the book differs from a whole host of KJV's, save that it has a transparent dust jacket ("keeps the Bible looking like a Bible"), three color pictures, a glossary of terms (the third of which, curiously enough, is "adulteri"), paragraphing and a preface.

My purpose, however, is not to pan *The Teen-Age Version of the Holy Bible.* At their price the publishers are going to have a rough enough time as it is. Instead, I pay tribute to it for suggesting a whole new dimension of Bible publishing, capable of considerably greater daring.

I see, for example, *The Executive's Bible,* so stamped (tastefully, to be sure), shaped like a brief case, and edited to suit the needs and purposes of its constituency. Certain portions of the text will be deleted, i.e. "You cannot serve God and mammon" (Luke 16:13). Certain other portions will be printed in bold-face type: "Make friends for yourselves by

From *The Collected Writings of St. Hereticus,* ed. Robert McAfee Brown. Copyright © 1964, W. L. Jenkins. Philadelphia: The Westminster Press. Used by permission.

means of unrighteous mammon" (Luke 16:9) just happens to come to mind. For an extra $2.95 *The Executive's Bible* will have bound into its gray flannel lining a copy of Bruce Barton's *The Man Nobody Knows* (just reissued in a new edition), a book that should occupy almost equal canonical status in the life of the Executive.

Special attention can be given to the Executive's Golden Text, "Wist ye not that I must be about my Father's *business?*" (Luke 2:49), a bit of Scripture that made a very, very deep impression upon Mr. Barton. Another verse for bold-face treatment would be that one designed for contemplation when one's competitors have stolen a market: "I hate them with perfect hatred; I count them my enemies" (Psalm 139:22). We will of course excise reference to the fact that the early Christian community "had all things common, and sold their possessions and goods, and parted them to all men, as every man had need" (Acts 2:44–45). Smacks of Marx. Further reminder: no red covers on *The Executive's Bible.*

Another "must" is *The Sportsman's Bible,* for use on fishing trips and hunting expeditions. A waterproof jacket lined with kapok is called for, complete with built-in compass. The book will contain biblical maxims dear to the heart of sportsmen (the Psalmist's injunction to "Praise the Lord with pipes," etc.), a four-color painting for tennis enthusiasts of Joseph serving in Pharaoh's court (detachable so that it may be mounted, framed and hung in the den), an etching of the hart panting after the water brooks, perhaps pursued by a Christian hunter, and a glossary of all the times the word "fish" is mentioned in the Bible. Protestant and Catholic consultants could be polled in advance about the advisability of including biblical instances of determining the divine will by a throw of the dice. Printed in capital letters or italics could be the Pauline advice, "Use a little wine for the sake of your stomach" (I Timothy 5:23).

For publication in time for the 1964 fall campaigns could be a special edition of *The Politician's Bible.* This should be bound in scuffed leather to give the impression of wear and tear incurred by daily use. On the flyleaf could be inscribed, in a simulated feminine scrawl, "To my dear son. . . ." The size of the volume (25/8″ × 43/4″) should occasion such press dispatches as, "Whipping his well-worn Bible, a gift from his mother, out of his vest pocket, the candidate replied. . . ."

References to kings and other national leaders being punished for failing to do the will of God will of course be deleted, along with embarrassing passages like Revelation 13 that compare the state to the beast. This will enable greater prominence to be given to the biblical insight that a "ruler" (i.e., a politician) is "God's servant for your good."

Politicians advocating a certain type of fiscal policy will want the authority of Holy Writ for their admonition to "Pay . . . taxes to whom taxes are due" (Romans 13:7). And all politicians, by conflating certain texts with a minimum of dishonesty, will be able to claim direct scriptural warrant for the stock-in-trade conclusion of every political speech, viz. "This . . . nation . . . under . . . God" (cf. respectively Esther 9:17, Isaiah 1:4, Genesis 1:7, 2 Kings 1:2. New Testament references will be made available in the future for politicians not primarily concerned with "the Jewish vote").

In spite of its limited market at present, work should commence immediately on my newest high-priority project: *The Astronaut's Bible.* But this requires more space than is available at present.

GOD IS DEAD IN GEORGIA

Eminent Deity Succumbs During Surgery—Succession in Doubt As All Creation Groans

LBJ ORDERS FLAGS AT HALF STAFF

Anthony Towne

SPECIAL TO THE NEW YORK TIMES

ATLANTA GA., Nov. 9—God, creator of the universe, principal deity of the world's Jews, ultimate reality of Christians, and most eminent of all divinities, died late yesterday during major surgery undertaken to correct a massive diminishing influence. His exact age is not known, but close friends estimate that it greatly exceeded that of all other extant beings. While he did not, in recent years, maintain any fixed abode, his house was said to consist of many mansions.

The cause of death could not be immediately determined, pending an autopsy, but the deity's surgeon, Thomas J. J. Altizer, 38, of Emory University in Atlanta, indicated possible cardiac insufficiency. Assisting Dr. Altizer in the unsuccessful surgery were Dr. Paul van Buren of Temple University, Philadelphia; Dr. William Hamilton of Colgate-Rochester, Rochester, N.Y.; and Dr. Gabriel Vahanian of Syracuse University, Syracuse, N.Y.

Word of the death, long rumored, was officially disclosed to

173

reporters at five minutes before midnight after a full day of mounting anxiety and the comings and going of ecclesiastical dignitaries and members of the immediate family. At the bedside, when the end came, were, in addition to the attending surgeons and several nurses, the Papal Nuncio to the United States, representing His Holiness, Pope Paul VI, Vicar of Christ on Earth and Supreme Pontiff of the Roman Catholic Church; Iakovos, Archbishop of North and South America, representing the Orthodox Churches; Dr. Eugene Carson Blake, Stated Clerk of the Presbyterian Church in the USA, representing the World Council of Churches, predominantly a Protestant institution; Rabbi Mark Tannenbaum of New York City, representing the tribes of Israel, chosen people, according to their faith, of the deceased; The Rev. William Moyers, Baptist minister, representing President Johnson; the 3rd Secretary of the Soviet embassy in Trinidad, representing the Union of Soviet Socialist Republics; and a number of unidentified curious bystanders.

Unable to be in Atlanta owing to the pressure of business at the second Vatican Council, now in session, the Pope, in Rome, said, in part: "We are deeply distressed for we have suffered an incalculable loss. The contributions of God to the Church cannot be measured, and it is difficult to imagine how we shall proceed without Him." Rumors swept through the Council, meeting under the great vaulted dome of St. Peter's, that, before adjourning the Council in December, the Pope will proclaim God a saint, an action, if taken, that would be wholly without precedent in the history of the Church. Several aged women were reported to have come forward with claims of miraculous cures due to God's intervention. One woman, a 103 year old Bulgarian peasant, is said to have conceived a son at the very instant God expired. Proof of miracles is a precondition for sanctification according to ancient tradition of the Roman Catholic faith.

In Johnson City, Texas, President Johnson, recuperating from his recent gall bladder surgery, was described by aides as "profoundly upset." He at once directed that all flags should be at half-staff until after the funeral. The First Lady and the two presidential daughters, Luci and Lynda, were understood to have wept openly. Luci, 18, the younger daughter, whose engagement has been lately rumored, is a convert to Roman Catholicism. It is assumed that the President and his family, including his cousin, Oriole, will attend the last rites, if the international situation permits. Both houses of Congress met in Washington at noon today and promptly adjourned after passing a joint resolution expressing "grief and great respect for the departed spiritual leader." Sen. Wayne Morse, Dem. of Oregon, objected on the grounds that the resolution violated the principle of separation of church and state, but he was overruled by Vice President Hubert Humphrey, who remarked that "this is not a time for partisan politics."

Plans for the deity's funeral are incomplete. Reliable sources suggested that extensive negotiations may be necessary in order to select a church for the services and an appropriate liturgy. Dr. Wilhelm Pauck, theologian, of Union Seminary in New York City proposed this morning that it would be "fitting and seemly" to inter the remains in the ultimate ground of all being, but it is not known whether that proposal is acceptable to the family. Funerals for divinities, common in ancient times, have been exceedingly rare in recent centuries, and it is understood that the family wishes to review details of earlier funerals before settling upon rites suitable for God.

(In New York, meanwhile, the stock market dropped sharply in early trading. Volume was heavy. One broker called it the most active market day since the assassination of President Kennedy, Nov. 22, 1963. The market rallied in late trading, after reports were received that Jesus—see 'Man in the News,' p. 36, col. 4—who survives, plans to assume a larger role in management of the universe.)

Reaction from the world's great and from the man in the street was uniformly incredulous. "At least he's out of his misery," commented one housewife in an Elmira, N.Y., supermarket. "I can't believe it," said the Right Reverend Horace W. B. Donegan, Protestant Episcopal Bishop of New York, who only last week celebrated the 15th anniversary of his installation as Bishop. In Paris, President de Gaulle, in a 30 second appearance on national television, proclaimed: "God is dead! Long live the republic! Long live France!" Mrs. Jacqueline Kennedy, widow of the late President, was reported "in seclusion" in her Fifth Avenue apartment. "She's had about all she can take," a close friend of the Kennedy family said. News of the death was included in a one sentence statement, without comment, on the 3rd page of Pravda, official organ of the Soviet government. The passing of God has not been disclosed to the 800 million Chinese who live behind the bamboo curtain.

Public reaction in this country was perhaps summed up by an elderly retired streetcar conductor in Passaic, New Jersey, who said: "I never met him, of course. Never even saw him. But from what I heard I guess he was a real nice fellow. Tops." From Independence, Mo., former President Harry S. Truman, who received the news in his Kansas City barbershop, said: "I'm always sorry to hear somebody is dead. It's a damn shame." In Gettysburg, Pa., former President Dwight D. Eisenhower, released, through a military aide, the following statement: "Mrs. Eisenhower joins me in heartfelt sympathy to the family and many friends of the late God. He was, I always felt, a force for moral good in the universe. Those of us who were privileged to know him admired the probity of his character, the breadth of his compassion, the depth of his intellect. Generous almost to a fault, his many acts of kindness to America will never be forgotten. It is a very great loss indeed. He will be missed."

From Basel, Switzerland, came word that Dr. Karl Barth, venerable Protestant theologian, informed of the death of God, declared: "I don't know who died in Atlanta, but whoever he was he's an imposter." Dr. Barth, 79, with the late Paul Tillich, is widely regarded as the foremost theologian of the 20th Century.

(There have been unconfirmed reports that Jesus of Nazareth, 33, a carpenter and reputed son of God, who survives, will assume the authority, if not the title, of the deceased deity. Jesus, sometimes called the Christ, was himself a victim of death, having succumbed some 1932 years ago in Palestine, now the state of Israel, purportedly on orders of a Roman governor, Pontius Pilate, and at the behest of certain citizens of Jerusalem. This event, described by some as 'deicide,' has lately occupied the deliberations of the Vatican Council, which has solemnly exonerated the Jews generally of responsibility for the alleged crime. The case is complicated by the fact that Jesus, although he died, returned to life, and so may not have died at all. Diplomats around the world were speculating today on the place the resurrected Jesus will occupy in the power vacuum created by the sudden passing of God.)

Dr. Altizer, God's surgeon, in an exclusive interview with the Times, stated this morning that the death was "not unexpected." "He had been ailing for some time," Dr. Altizer said, "and lived much longer than most of us thought possible." He noted that the death of God had, in fact, been prematurely announced in the last century by the famed German surgeon, Nietzsche. Nietzsche, who was insane the last ten years of his life, may have confused "certain symptoms of morbidity in the aged patient with actual death, a mistake any busy surgeon will occasionally make," Dr. Altizer suggested. "God was an excellent patient, compliant, cheerful, alert. Every comfort modern science could provide was made available to him. He did not suffer—he just, as it were, slipped out of our grasp." Dr. Altizer also disclosed that plans for a memorial to God have already been discussed informally, and it is likely a committee of eminent clergymen and laymen will soon be named to raise funds for use in "research into the causes of death in deities, an area of medicine many physicians consider has been too long neglected." Dr. Altizer indicated, finally, that he had great personal confidence that Jesus, relieved of the burdens of divinity, would, in time, assume a position of great importance in the universe. "We have lost," he said, "a father, but we have gained a son."

(Next Sunday's New York Times will include, without

177

extra charge, a 24-page full-color supplement with many photographs, reviewing the major events of God's long reign, the circumstances of his sudden and untimely death, and prospects for a godless future. The editors will be grateful for pertinent letters, photographs, visions and the like.)

There has been as yet no statement from Jesus, but a close associate, the Holy Ghost, has urged prayer and good works. He also said that it is the wish of the family that in lieu of flowers contributions be made to the Building Fund for the Cathedral of St. John the Divine in New York City so that the edifice may be finished.

For Further Reading

The following works are suggested as supplementary reading which places religious satire within a broad literary context.

Allen, Charles A. *Satire*. Belmont, Calif.: Wadsworth Publishing Co., Inc., 1962.

Auden, W. H. "Notes on the Comic." *Thought*, XXVII (1952), pp. 57–61.

Blair, Walter. *Native American Humor*. San Francisco: Chandler Publishing Co., 1960.

Carlisle, Henry C., Jr., ed. *American Satire in Prose and Verse*. New York: Random House, Inc., 1962.

Cazamian, Louis. *The Development of English Humor*. Durham, N.C.: Duke University Press, 1952.

Clark, A. M. "The Art of Satire and the Satiric Spectrum." *Studies in Literary Modes*. London: Oliver, 1946.

Davies, Horton. *A Mirror of the Ministry in Modern Novels*. Oxford, England: Oxford University Press, 1959.

Elliot, Robert. *The Power of Satire*. Princeton, N.J.: Princeton University Press, 1961.

Enck, John, ed. *The Comic in Theory and Practice*. New York: Appleton-Century Co., 1961

Feinberg, Leonard. *The Satirist*. Ames: Iowa State University Press, 1963.

Fiedler, Leslie. *No! In Thunder*. Boston: Beacon Press, 1960.

Frye, Northrop. *Anatomy of Criticism*. Princeton, N.J.: Princeton University Press, 1957.

179

For Further Reading

Fuller, B. A. G. "Is Reality Really Comic?" *Journal of Philosophy*, XLIII (1946), p. 589.

Hall, James. *The Tragic Comedians*. Bloomington: Indiana University Press, 1963.

Hannay, James. *Satire and Satirists*. New York: The Viking Press, 1949.

Highet, Gilbert. *An Anatomy of Satire*. Princeton, N.J.: Princeton University Press, 1961.

Hopkins, Kenneth. *Portraits in Satire*. London: Cunningham, 1958.

Johnson, Edgar, ed. *A Treasury of Satire*. New York: Simon and Schuster, Inc., 1945.

Kelling, Harold. "Reason in Madness." *PMLA*, LXIX (1954).

Kernan, Alvin. *The Cankered Muse: Satire of the English Renaissance*. New Haven, Conn.: Yale University Press, 1959.

Knox, Ronald. *Essays in Satire*. London: Sheed & Ward, Ltd., 1928.

————. "On Humour and Satire," *New and Old Essays*. London: Sheed & Ward, Ltd., 1937.

Leyburn, Ellen. *Satiric Allegory: Mirror of Man*. New Haven, Conn.: Yale University Press, 1956.

Lowrey, Burling. *Twentieth Century Parody*. New York: Harcourt, Brace and Company, Inc., 1960.

Mack, Maynard. "The Muse of Satire." *Yale Review*, XLI (1951), p. 90.

Mumford, Lewis. *The Mood of Satire*. San Francisco: W. H. Freeman & Co., Publishers, 1923.

Potter, Stephen. *Sense of Humor*. London: Reinhardt, 1954.

Priestly, J. B. *English Humour*. London: Longmans, 1929.

Scott, Nathan. "The Bias of Comedy." *The Christian Scholar*, XLIV (1961).

Seldes, Gilbert. "The Death of Satire." *New Republic*, Jan. 5, 1927.

Spears, M. K. "Late Auden: The Satirist as a Lunatic Clergyman." *Sewanee Review*, LIX (1951), p. 56.

For Further Reading

Swabey, M. C. *Comic Laughter*. New Haven, Conn.: Yale University Press, 1961.

Walker, Hugh. *English Satirists and Satire*. London: J. M. Dent & Sons, Ltd., 1925.

Worcester, David. *The Art of Satire*. Cambridge, England: University Press, 1960.

Vulliamy, C. E. *The Anatomy of Satire*. London: Michael Joseph, Ltd., 1950.

Zuver, Dudley. *Salvation by Laughter*. New York: Harper and Brothers, 1933.